Health Care Policy in Ireland

A Study in Control

David McKevitt
School of Management
Open University

RA
395
.I73
M35
1990

ISBN	1873112 09
Copyright	David McKevitt
Publisher	Hibernian University Press

CONTENTS

LIST OF TABLES

FOREWORD

Leonard Wrigley

This study of the control of public health care systems by
David McKevitt has its origins in both a practical problem and a
theoretical problem, and still bears the hall mark of its birth
pangs. Because of its origins, it constitutes a significant
contribution to the debate on the appropriate system for the
provision of public health care service in a civilized society,
where citizens demand good health care facilities, freely
available to all those in need, where voters demand a limit to the
amount of money paid in taxation, and where medical specialists
demand the resources proper to their professional calling. It is
especially relevant to the debate in Ireland, both because the
study was of the Irish public health care service, and because in
Ireland the debate itself has been lifted high off the ground - to
the level of those happy uplands, where all good things seem
possible, everywhere, at all times - and needs to be brought
down to the arena of practical possibilities.

The practical problem, essentially, was queueing for a medical
facility: how to contain, control, and, if possible, reduce the size
of the queue for the services of the radiology unit in Cork
Regional Hospital. In the first place the problem came to me.
Early in 1985, I was requested by the Irish Southern Health
Board to serve as a consultant to the Cork Regional Hospital,
where the queue for radiology was large, and getting larger, and
where there were complaints from those in the queue that they
were waiting too long for treatment. At the time I was employed
by University College Cork (UCC), serving as AIB Professor of
Management and Head of the Management Department, and
Dean of the Commerce faculty, Director of MBA programme, as
well as a member of seventeen college committees, so was well
tied up. But the problem of the hospital seemed in all essentials
like all the problems I knew about in the college, namely, how to
allocate scarce resources amongst a whole range of desirable
things, for each of which there was virtually an unlimited
demand. I thought it would be both interesting and challenging
to tackle the hospital problem. I also felt obliged to respond to a

call from those who care for the sick. By good fortune, there was then available in the Management Department a newly enrolled Doctoral candidate, one who had significant experience of the Irish public services, as well as an outstanding scholastic record, namely David McKevitt. He agreed to tackle the problem (subject only to the condition that his Phd thesis might be in the same area). For a year or so, he worked as a consultant in the Cork Regional Hospital, gathering data from patients, medical specialists, and from administrative personnel, and eventually wrote a report on the nature of the problem, and what should be done to solve it. From this ground floor experience, David McKevitt decided that his Phd thesis should be focussed on the control of public health care.

The theoretical problem came from the literature on Management, where there was a lacuna in the area concerned with the control of those institutions, like Health, Education, and Welfare, which provide services without charge to all those who need them. Perhaps lacuna is not the right word. Much that is currently written in that area contain, it seems to me, the assumptions and logic of a lunatic asylum. It is not at all surprising that everywhere today socialism is at bay. In the event, there is a problem in the theory concerned with the control of those public services where the need is virtually unlimited, but where the necessary finance has to be provided from taxation. And until this theoretical problem is properly tackled, the actual control of public health, education and welfare is essentially blind and undirected in any steps beyond those guided by habit and tradition. David McKevitt, with his lifelong committment to social democracy, and his experience in the public services (including a turn as Assistant Registrar of University College Cork), was determined to use his Phd studies to make some attempt to contribute to the literature.

The present study, therefore, has its roots in real problems, and is much the richer for that. Its big message - and let there be no doubt about it - is that ultimate control must lie in the legislature and the law courts. Dr. McKevitt wants the right to public health care to be enshrined in law. If that is granted, then the users (the sick) who have a complaint can take their case to the law courts. At least, he is totally honest. What is the point of the present literature, with its bland assumption of public 'rights' to free health care, education and welfare, if these rights cannot be enforced at law. But whether Irish society is yet ready to receive such a message is a question Dr. McKevitt has himself chosen to avoid. The reader should, however, be prepared to confront that question.

In private enterprise the ultimate control of the working of any particular firm lies with the customers and the competitors in the market place, more exactly, with the tastes and budgets of customers, and with the strategy and production costs of competitors. The legitimacy and effectiveness of the control system within each particular firm is derived from this; from customer's budgets and competitor's costs. There is, today, no equivalent source for the legitimacy and effectiveness of the control system in public health care. If we reject the message of Dr. McKevitt, then either we proceed as heretofore with control systems without legitimacy or effectiveness, or we turn health care over to private enterprise. The reader should be prepared to confront that too.

The present study, as a Phd thesis, was completed prior to the publication in 1989 by the government of the report on the financing of Irish health care, under the chairmanship of Dr. Hederman O'Brien. The Hederman O'Brien report stressed the importance of the control systems, but avoided the central issues in control, as was justified, since the question of finance and of control are logically and in practice quite different. Nevertheless, the existence in the same time-frame of these two studies should serve to bring down to earth the debate in Ireland on the appropriate system for the provision of public health care services.

I was glad to have been the supervisor of Dr. McKevitt's Phd thesis, and am delighted it is now to be published. Ireland has few doctoral thesis in the social sciences. This situation is very different from that in other countries, including those small modern countries, like Denmark, New Zealand, and Switzerland. Ireland needs many more social sciences studies like the present, which are grounded in practice and theory, which are developed as works of scholarship, for a Phd, and which are then published for the practitioners in the field, the academics in the classroom, and the civil servants in the government.

Leonard Wrigley   May 1990

ACKNOWLEDGEMENTS

My immediate debt is to the many people in the health services, both in Ireland and aboard who have given of their time to assist me. Officials in the Departments of Health and Finance, and in the voluntary hospitals and health boards were most co-operative in my endless requests for data. I thank them for this, and I am more grateful, than I suspect they realize. Here I wish to record a particular debt to Mr. Peter Gaffey, Mr. Jerry O'Dwyer and Mr. Oliver Cussen.

During the research in the Department of Management in University College, Cork, I was supported by Lil Courtney and by Brian McNulty and by the other researchers in the Department, Ray Murphy, Nora Hennessy, Shula Wrigley and Aine Hurley. I wish to pay tribute to this support and to their patience with me in my bad times. Professor Leonard Wrigley, who directed the research, vigorously "front loaded" the research design and encouraged me to persist with a well tried research methodology. His scholarship and integrity were at all times a challenge and example to the researchers in the Department of Management.

I wish also to pay tribute to the staff of the Cork Regional Hospital who bore with me during the consultancy there, particularly Professor W.O. Kirwan, Dr. Michael Hurley and Mr. Joe Martin. I wish to pay special tribute to Dr. Liam McFeeley for his committed support over the entire research. Dr. J. K. Barry was also supportive during the research. Margaret McGovern bore patiently with the many drafts of the text.

The research was funded by FMC (Ireland), and by the consultancy funds of the Management Department in UCC; I acknowledge this support; the research could not have been completed without it - particularly the foreign travel and I am grateful to FMC, the Management Department, and the Finance Office, UCC.

The effort would not have been sustainable without the support of Una and Martha.

CHAPTER ONE

Introduction

This study examines the development of the health service in Ireland from 1970 to 1987 and its primary focus is the investment in acute hospital services. Ireland's record is compared with other European countries as it is clear that the problems posed by control of health care systems is not a phenomenon unique to Ireland. Indeed, one of this study's central conclusions is the extent to which the lessons of other countries were not incorporated into Ireland's investment decision-making and the disregard of the valuable experience of other European countries successful strategies for control of their health care expenditures.

At the core of health expenditures and the State's attempt to control their growth is the assumption that the money is properly managed and that it is effective in achieving its objectives. Underlying this assumption is the concern that "proper control" is difficult to achieve and that, in some manner, the money spent is not being used to best effect. The evaluation of effectiveness can take a number of forms. First, that there is effective financial control so that the money is spent and accounted for in accordance with legislative or regulatory policy. Second, that the money is used in a manner supportive of the policy of the legislature or control department to achieve specific objectives; for example, that hospital expenditures are properly managed so as to contain overall costs and allow for some re-allocation to other areas of the health care system such as primary and community care. Third, and most intractable, that the money is not being diverted or captured by health care workers (in wage increases over and above some national accepted level of fairness) to the detriment of patient care expenditure.

Public expenditure on health services, together with other areas of social expenditure such as education, service a number of quite distinct policy objectives. In health, for example, these objectives range from control of communicable diseases through to the modernisation of diagnostic facilities on a par with other, more advanced, economies than Ireland. These objectives are funded through a mix of general taxation, public and private health insurance schemes and services are provided in profit and not-for-profit health care institutions. The range of policy objectives and the consequent organisational diversity produces a complex system which requires a central control mechanism to ensure compliance between expenditure and specific policy objectives. This study argues that Ireland, unlike other European countries, lacks this essential control mechanism which would order policy objectives, review performance and bring the health care system into balance with stated policy objectives. Control of health costs, and in particular hospital costs, is high on the agenda for debate in every modern country. The specific characteristics of the debate vary from country to country and are related to the economic circumstances of the time, the organisational framework for the delivery of health services, the relative contribution of public and private revenues for health service provision and the role of the State in the organisation of the health service. Solutions advanced range from the strategic - a reduction in the health care system - to structural change - greater private provision of health services, through to operational improvements such as greater efficiency in the delivery of health services[1].

FIGURE 1.2

OUTLINE ORGANISATION FOR DEPARTMENT OF HEALTH 1973

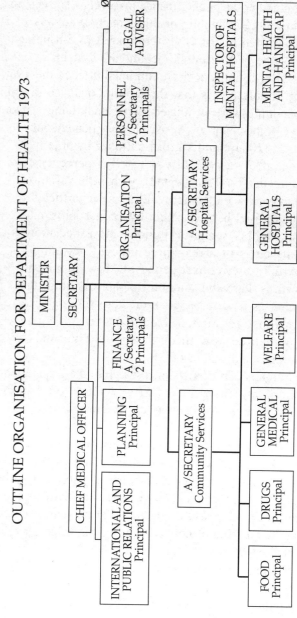

ø Shared with Departments of Local Government and Social Welfare.

Source: Department of Health: Restructuring the Department of Health, 1973

In Ireland, control of public health-care is important because of the magnitude of the public finance involved. The cost to the government budget of public health-care in 1986 was £1,300 million or 7.5 percent of GNP (compared to 5.8 percent in Denmark for the Danish public health-care system)[2]. Health expenditures have, indeed, risen continually since the 1960's. What is of importance is that this continuous rise in public health expenditure was not related to the underlying economic performance of the country. As Wrigley has pointed out:

> Since 1820, Ireland's gross national income has grown at or just slightly below 1.5 percent per annum (the 1960's excepted), with little variation beyond wars and trade cycles.... Nevertheless, Ireland raised her per capita living standards, and developed her social institutions and expectations on the basis of a real three percent per annum growth.... A consequence of slow economic growth is that valid solutions to shortrun problems require, as it were, a series of 'zero sum games'. Solutions requiring finance can only be implemented now through a redistribution of existing wealth and income[3].

This research is part of a wider research in the Department of Management at University College Cork on Ireland's competitiveness in the world at large. The original propositions of that wider research were twofold; first, that Ireland, to make progress, must learn from the successful small modern economies like Denmark. Second, that Ireland must learn how to improve the quality of her investment in public and private enterprise. These propositions have now been narrowed to the investment decision process. Hence, the present research is centred on the question of how to improve the value for money in public health services.

The non-capital spending on statutory health services for the period 1971-1987 is set out in Table 1.1. The public sector borrowing requirement (PSBR) for the period 19975-1986 is set out in Table 1.2. The official stance on the relationship between State spending on the health services and the economic conditions necessary to support them has undergone significant adjustment. On the introduction of the Health Bill in 1969, which sought to implement the re-organisation of health services, the Minister for Health stated "the present government has not accepted the proposition that the State had a duty to provide unconditionally all medical, dental and other health service free of cost for everyone. Their policy has always been to design the services and the provisions on eligibility for them on the basis that a person should not be denied medical care because of lack of means, but that the services should not be free for all"[4]. In the same debate, an opposition spokesman said "it is possible for our community, as it has been for all communities in Europe, with the exception of the Laps in Finland, to organise a health service which would entitle everybody, as of right, to get medical services without charge at time of need"[5]. Clearly, at that time, government spending on health services was considered a desirable political objective.

Because of a change in political climate, the relationship between public expenditure and corresponding improvements in national health status is now being vigorously questioned. For example, the Department of Health's document 'Health - The Wider Dimensions' (December, 1986) states: "it is a matter of concern that despite the increasing level of national resources devoted to health services over the past two decades, the level of health in the population did not show any marked improvement"[6]. The National Economic and Social Council (NESC) document "Strategy for Development 1986-1990", while also querying the relationship between health expenditures and improvements in health, recommends changes in the institutional arrangements for health-care provision. The NESC commented that Ireland shared the same problems as other health-care systems: "contemporary health regimes originated in large-scale institutional/hospital provision which is relatively expensive: the orientation and training of medical manpower is, to a considerable extent, geared to hospital-based care and to the use of expensive, highly technological, procedures; until recently the relative importance of more economic, non-institutional, care and preventative programmes was not fully appreciated"[7]. In 1987, the Minister for Health stated "the background is that everybody in the country believes it necessary to curtail public expenditure. The national debt is currently costing us £2.5 billion per annum to service, and we are continuing to borrow for day-to-day spending. The point is that you can't fully curtail public expenditure without impinging on the health services"[8].

The decision to reduce expenditure on the Irish health service was not accompanied by orderly or systematic review of selected areas or programmes for appropriate reduction. The reduction, expressed by the Department of Finance as a global expenditure figure and translated by the Department of Health into an equivalent manpower reduction, was then applied **pro rata** across the eight health boards and voluntary hospitals. No policy objectives were issued by the centre to assist the organisations in their management of the reduced budgets, other than "front-line staff should be protected". In large measure, the applications of cuts was a crude process because of the severe underdevelopment of the Irish health information data-base. It was also a result of unarticulated policy objectives and rigidities in the resource allocation mechanism. This was the consequence of over ten years of sustained growth in health-care expenditures which was not accompanied by any regard to the strategic basis for this investment decision. Ireland, unlike the other countries examined in this study, did not attend to the basic questions on health-care policy - what were its aims, who was to benefit, and how was progress to be monitored?

The policy proposals contained in both the NESC and in the Department of Health documents argue that the existing institutional basis of the health-care system must be changed. Over half of current expenditure is spent on institutional services, and in relation to that, the Department of Health seeks to move the emphasis from hospitals towards community-based services. However, the criteria for the reallocation of resources is not specified. Clearly, the total cost of the health service, relative to our economic performance, is now being widely questioned by government. Also, questioned by government are the improvements in health-care in line with the increases in cost and, indeed, the effectiveness of the health-care system as a whole. Thus, there is a general perception amongst those who allocate public finance that there is a real and important problem in Ireland of control of the Irish public health-care system.

Information lies at the heart of the debate on control. In the case of a health-care system, such information would include financial control but it must, to be effective, extend well beyond this functional test. In the case of acute hospitals, measurement would embrace quality of care, morbidity, patient satisfaction, and cost-effective medical decision-making. It will be shown, however, that in Ireland measurement never got beyond the functional test of financial control and that, even here, it was weak.

The study's focus on acute hospitals within the Irish health-care system is for three major reasons. First, acute hospital expenditure accounts for some fifty percent (50%) of total current health expenditures of £1.3 billion. Despite policy statements on the need for a re-orientation of the system, it has not yet proved possible to significantly alter the hospital sector's share of national health resources. Second, hospital policy in Ireland was the subject of detailed discussion and examination from 1968 onwards and in 1987 national policy was still unresolved. Third, hospitals and hospital treatment represents the core problem of the technology-cost-value matrix in modern medicine. A study of hospitals is, therefore, a study of the central challenge faced by government, taxpayers and the medical profession.

A central theme of studies on hospitals has been the extent to which their provision worldwide has become a major State activity. Some commentators have argued, **a priori,** that the relative absence of a private hospital sector inhibits competition and, hence, leads to inefficiencies in the cost of hospital services. Proponents of State provision have argued that private, for-profit, hospitals capture the lucrative end of the market (aided by third-party insurance schemes) and that they do not have social and equity objectives as do State hospitals.

While the theme of professional dominance in medical care is a much-repeated nostrum, it does provide some useful economic insight into the dynamics of health-care systems. More important, perhaps, are the social and personal implications of this phenomenon both for the medical profession and health-care managers. If there are no agreed aims or objectives in health policy in the context of national or regional provision, and if medical consultants dominate the training of junior doctors, then it is likely that a hospital model will be dominant in national health-care provision. This may well also induce in the patient, taxpayer and regulatory agency, an artificial coalition of interests, where the asymmetry of information, access and revenue, will result in no change to the basic values of the system. March and Simon put it as follows:

> Where goals are ostensibly shared (e.g. profit maximisation) but not operational, then two subcases need to be distinguished, a distinction that is significant for the character of the decision-making process. The shared goals may be held in common because they have been internalised by members of the executive group; or, there may be common organisational goals that the executive accept because of the reward structure. In the former case, we would expect a good deal of ideological conflict in the bargaining process - genuine disagreement as to which means will best implement the goals. In the latter case, we would expect bargaining to be of a more opportunistic sort, characterised by rationalisations attempting to "clothe private aims with a public interest".[9]

March and Simon go on to observe that "the prevalence of bargaining is a symptom either that the goals are not operational or that they are not shared". The policy on development of the acute Irish hospital sector, discussed in detail in Chapter Four, supports the contention that there was no agreement on the goals of the hospital sector relative to other parts of the health-care system. This did not preclude, however, a sustained record of resourcing the hospital sector.

Despite the magnitude of the finance involved, there has not, as far as is known, been in Ireland a serious exploration within a well-grounded theoretical framework that links policy objectives, performance measurement and investment decisions in the health care system as a whole. Clearly, there is a need for an analysis that would contribute to the clarification of these issues, an analysis structured in such a way as to provide some comparative data on how other countries confront the common problem of control of publicly-financed health-care. The present study springs from that need.

For a general theoretical framework, the Business Policy model developed by Bruce Scott in his DBA thesis, An Open System Model of the Firm (Harvard 1963) and applied in the study of industrial planning in France, is used to consider the present arrangements for control in the Irish health-care system. The model asserts that:

(1) Any organisation relates to its environment via a strategy for advancing its interests as it perceives these interests;

(2) the interests of the various sub-units of an organisation often differ from those of the organisation as a whole; and

(3) thus the central or general headquarters of the organisation must bring continuous influence to bear on the sub-units in order to motivate them to act in conformity with the general or shared interests of the organisation.[10]

Scott went on to note that the most important forms of influence are: the ability to allocate resources, to establish and alter organisational structures, to measure and reward performance, and to formulate policy limits or "rules of the games". (It should be noted that this model was developed in relation to business firms and subsequently used by Scott in relation to a nation state).

The objective of the present study is to examine the validity of the following set of propositions:

(1) The Irish health-care system has developed as a government-financed activity, yet it has operated without an objective statement of its mission.

(2) Because of the lack of an objective statement of the mission of the Irish health-care system, the general hospital segment, either public or voluntary, has no defined role, or no rational system of resource allocation.

(3) Because the general hospital control system has no objective norms:

(a) resource allocation is highly centralised in Dublin and the system lacks responsiveness to local health needs in the remainder of Ireland;

(b) the professionals within hospitals have created slack and captured that slack for their own benefit, and

(c) there is no impetus to clarify the mission of the health-care system as a whole.

The research propositions are tested using data from a number of sources. The legislative basis of Irish health-care and that of other European countries is examined to see what guidelines or policy it contains that would assist health-care managers and medical personnel in their work. Second, data on health-care spending and resource allocation is examined and the relationship between programme objectives and their effectiveness explored. Third, the study utilises data from interviews with health-care managers and medical personnel in Ireland, Sweden and the Netherlands to give the experience of people directly involved in the day-to-day task of health-care delivery.

Expenditure on health services and the policies that government adopt for health care provision reflect widely divergent opinions as to the role of the State in the provision of medical care. The countries examined in this study - Ireland, Sweden, and the Netherlands - differ in such matters as the financial support given by way of central taxation, the local administrative arrangements for service delivery and the regulation of private health-care provision. It is not contended that either Sweden or the Netherlands represent an "ideal solution" to the provision of health services. Indeed, given the very nature of 'health' and the attitudes towards death in modern social democratic nations, it is highly unlikely that any country can satisfy public expectations of the efficacy of modern medical practice. However, a comparable focus provides data on how these countries confront the common problems of public health services. A central stance of this study is that Ireland has neglected the common experience of these countries, particularly in its disregard for the sovereign importance of an investment decision framework which relates public expenditure to specific policy objectives. The primary requirement is a legislative framework for health-care policy that facilitates resource allocation directed towards specific health-care programmes. Such a requirement is independent of the particular policy choices adopted by government towards, for example, public or private health-care insurance as the data for Sweden and the Netherlands demonstrates (see Chapter Four). Moreover, the pre-requisites for control are not linked to any specific ideological choice as to the form of health-care provision. Ireland is different from the other countries not in its organisation or its financial support, but in the absence of a control system that would facilitate implementation of stated government policy objectives in health-care provision. The study shows that Sweden and the Netherlands, unlike Ireland, exhibit common features in their regard for explicitness in health-care objectives, their development of performance measurement and information systems and their shared experience in using legislation as the basic strategy statement for health-care policy. In addition, both countries have pursued a decentralised form of administration which strongly contrasts with the Irish pattern of increasing centralisation.

In examining a period as recent as 1970-1987 for health-care, one must have regard to the enormous improvements in facilities in that time. Regard must also be paid to the efforts of successive administrations in shaping this development. It is also the case, however, that the rise in health-care expenditures, and the subsequent efforts to control them is the result of the interplay between quite powerful and well-organised coalitions - the civil service, health-care professionals, and hospital administrators - and that the basis of this relationship can obscure the ostensible purpose of the endeavour - improvement in the health status of the population. It is, therfore, quite apppropriate to examine the arguments that gave rise to the current problems of control from a perspective that focusses on the activities of professionals within a system that lacks external competition. As Barrington has observed: "the boom in private medicine has encouraged the appearance of separate private hospitals and clinics, independent of any public hospital or having little connection with a public hospital. What is not generally understood is the extent to which this trend has been encouraged by public subsidies and policies"[11]. The term 'professional' in this study embraces administrative, medical and para-medical staff in the health service. Much of the existing research in health-care organisations has concentrated on the medical professionals. The present research explores the relationship between the administrative 'centre' and the management structure in health board and voluntary hospitals. The focus on administrative implementation and professional compliance provides an alternative perspective to studies that concentrate on the process of government decision-making.

The present study represents a departure from the mainstream treatment of health-care policy in focussing on the State's investment decisions and its control system for the provision of public goods such as health-care. Hitherto, the dominant perspective has been that of the health-economist or the more qualitative tradition of social policy. The present focus on investment decisions springs from three main considerations. First, the predominant role, worldwide, of the State in financial support for health-care provisions (albeit that, in a federal or decentralised system, such support may be by way of local or regional tax). Second, the adoption in Ireland of a system of administrative control and compliance, in contrast to the conventional European model of legislative frameworks for important State investment decisions, may have led to inadequate or incomplete return on investment. The main effect of Ireland's administrative-based strategy can be seen in the severe underdevelopment of the health information data-base; thus, it is difficult to estimate the return on investment in the absence of relevant health-status information. Third, the strategic policy of redirecting resources to the primary care area is seen in Ireland as requiring no legislative change to refocus the State's resource allocation system. Such an administrative-based strategy runs counter to the experience of other European countries.

A proper legislative framework would also assist in the definition of the relationship between the public as taxpayer and as the recipient of State-funded services. It would, for example, be possible to establish a clearer contractual relationship between the State as provider and the public as the funder of the service. Such a relationship would most directly impact on the health service in the area of service provision, and would also assist in the problem of governance and accountability of the professionals within health-care who, in Ireland, are primarily State-funded employees. It would, as in other European countries, replace the informal, ad hoc controls of administrative or professional compliance by systematic, legislative-based, governance and establish a more focussed control system. The wider impact of this relationship is discussed in Chapter Eight.

In Ireland, unlike other European countries, undue emphasis has been placed on the form of the management account and stress has been placed on the mechanics of the accounting system. This is, of course, a necessary but not a sufficient condition for effective control. It is also the case, particularly in the publicly-managed sector, that even the mechanisms of control are considered ineffective[12].

Undue emphasis on the 'cost' of a service and the form of accounting procedures can lead to what Hopwood has described as the "routinisation of concern" with plans becoming more important than planning, budgets than the process of budgetting and costing than the ascertainment of costs"[13]. The need to account for spending also raises the issue of the basis on which the account is made. Thus, for example, the "cost" of hospital technology is seen as an important control challenge for the departments of Finance and Health, yet it is seen in a very different perspective by the medical consultants who utilise it. The professionals "need" the technology to improve the service to the client/patient. This clash of perspectives is described by Thompson as follows: "moreover, when the organisation incorporates larger numbers of professionals, the tendency is for them to insist that decision premises be set only by professionals, and this generates potential for conflict within the dominant coalition between professionals and others. Uneasiness seems to be characteristic of relations between professionals and lay administrators in research organisations, hospitals, universities, social welfare agencies and schools"[14]. In large measure, conflict within the Irish health-care system was absent due to the sustained allocation of resources from 1970 to 1980. The reduction in allocations, in particular in 1987, produced a very public conflict between the Minister for Health and his officials on the one hand, and medical staff and trade union interests on the other. The focus of the debate was money, but its nature was much more the result of unclear policy objectives than a reduction in the overdraft facilities of health boards and voluntary hospitals. That is, if money was to be reduced, then where was the reduction to take effect? Given the rigidity in the budget allocation process at the centre of government, the absence of legislation outlining clear policy objectives and the underdeveloped information system, the reductions were a rushed and divisive affair.

FOOTNOTES

1. For examples of the range of approaches specified, see Egdahl, "Should We Shrink the Health Care System", **Harvard Business Review,** Jan/Feb., 1984; Coddington, Palmquist and Trollinger "Strategies for Survival in the Hospital Industry", **Harvard Business Review,** May/June, 1985; Young and Saltman, "Preventive Medicine for Hospital Costs", **Harvard Business Review,** Jan/Feb., 1983.

2. Department of Health, **Health - The Wider Dimensions: A Consultative Statement on Health Policy,** 1986.

3. L. Wrigley, **Ireland's Economic Problems,** (unpublished), 1986.

4. **Dail Debates,** Vol. 239, April 1969, Column 1633.

5. Ibid, Column 1660.

6. **Health - The Wider Dimensions,** p.54.

7. National Economic and Social Council, **A Strategy for Development 1986-1990,** No. 83, November 1986, p.213.

8. **Aspect,** July/August 1987, p.12.

9. James G. March and Herbert A. Simon, **Organisations,** 1958, pp.196-197.

10. J. McArthur, and B.R. Scott, **Industrial Planning in France,** 1969, p.112.

11. R. Barrington, **Health Medicine and Politics in Ireland 1900-1970,** 1987, p.286.

12. For example, see **Appropriations Accounts 1982,** p.lix, where the Secretary of the Department of Health reports on the growth in the use of management consultants to improve the accounting systems in the health board structure. The same report (p.lviii) contains the Comptroller and Auditor General's statement that there was evidence of "serious operational lapses and deficiencies in accounting, internal control and security" in respect of the 1979 and 1980 accounts.

13. A. Hopwood, "Accounting and the Pursuit of Efficiency", p.183 in A. Hopwood and C. Tomkins (ed), **Issues in Public Sector Accounting,** 1984.

14. J.D. Thompson, **Organisations in Action,** 1967, p.139.

CHAPTER TWO

Health Care Planning in Ireland

The Irish acute hospital sector in 1989 is, in many respects, in its structure and management similar to that of the 1960's. It was never the intention of the Department of Health nor of the medical profession that it should be so. Thus, while resources, both capital and current, personnel and patients increased, the structure and organisation of the acute hospital sector did not change. Why? This chapter argues that the situation in the 1980's is a direct consequence of the failure to instal an effective control system in the Irish health-care system and that what should have been regarded as an experiment in administrative re-organisation became instead a rigid management system in an uncertain medical, social and economic environment. This chapter examines the major assumptions that underpinned the re-organisation of the Irish health services in 1970 and the control agencies that were set up to regulate and manage hospitals, i.e. the Regional Health Boards, Regional Hospital Boards and Comhairle na nOspideal (for consultant hospital staffing). The data presented form a preliminary test of the propositions that the Irish health care system lacks a clear mission and that decision-making is highly centralised. Particular emphasis is placed on the important unresolved issues which were not dealt with in legislation; for example, the co-ordination and control of the voluntary hospital sector (which is independent of State management) and the rationalisation of acute hospital services (recommended by the 1968 Report of the Consultative Council on the General Hospital Services). The Chapter also describes the concessions made during the passage of the legislation in the Dail which were to have significant impact on the control of the acute hospital sector.

Control is more than the functional task of accounting for expenditure. It is a social or ethical construct that brings coherence to the actions of individuals or units within an organisation. It brings, in Drucker's phrase, a 'social order' to the organisation which is far more than the sum of the individual parts of the accounting or information functions. That is, control disciplines and shapes the actions of the organisation and its personnel so that its strategy or policy is implemented. It is, therefore, a positive construct rather than a constraint on the behaviour of personnel and this study argues that the Irish health care system lacks such control. The description of the Swedish health care system (see Chapter Four) provides an example of a country where strategy and policy are implemented through an effective control system.

PAST AS PROLOGUE

The 1960's witnessed a number of investigations into the Irish health services and their organisation. In 1961, a Dail Committee was established to examine "to what extent the existing system of health services did not reasonably meet the essential medical needs of the population". The Committee met intermittently until it was wound up in 1965 - its report was never published but Barrington remarks that the Department of Health's own submissions to it formed the basis of the 1966 White Paper, "The Health Services and their Further Development"[1].

In 1967, A Consultative Committee, comprised in the main of medical consultants in the voluntary hospitals, was established "to examine the position in regard to general hospital in-patient and out-patient services in the State and to report in outline on the future organisation, extent and location of these services taking into account the changing pattern of demand, the impact of developing specialisation and the introduction of new techniques so as to secure, with due regard to the national resources, that the public is provided in the most effective way with the best possible services"[2]. The detailed recommendations of the Committee (popularly known as the Fitzgerald Committee after its Chairman, Professor Patrick Fitzgerald) are discussed below. The Committee recommended the regionalisation of hospital services, a reduction in the number of hospitals and beds and the establishment of a separate administrative system for hospital management. While the recommendations were never implemented in full, the report provided the impetus for a rapid growth in the hospital sector.

The basis of the Fitzgerald Committee's recommendations were, in essence, technocratic. Hospital medicine was becoming increasingly technology and science-based, excellence was seen as a function of size and complexity and the stock of hospitals and manpower in Ireland required renewal and expansion. Klein, in a study of the National Health Service in the United Kingdom, asserts that the intellectual highground was captured by the medical personnel whose arguments "set a boundary to the concepts of the feasible used by policy makers"[3]. In the Irish experience, the setting up of Comhairle na nOspideal with regulatory powers over the number and nature of medical consultant appointments, parallels the NHS case and, in large measure, the medical profession did imprint its own vision of the future on the re-organised health-care delivery system. That is, it was to be a hospital-centred system of health-care. In itself, this would not have been significant were it not for the fact that the hospital sector was significantly expanded in terms of capital employed, personnel and technology without the installation of an effective control system.

A review body, set up in 1972 to implement a restructuring of the Department of Health, stated in respect of the functions of Comhairle na nOspideal that: "in discharging its function on consultant appointments the Comhairle will fulfill a function which would otherwise be appropriate to the Minister. The Comhairle will be performing some of the most important functions of the health services since the range, quantity and quality of the service given by hospitals will be under its control"[4]. The influence of the Comhairle was not as wide as that suggested by the above, and the actions of the Comhairle was constrained by political and administrative considerations;

these are discussed in Chapters Five and Seven. Nevertheless, the system was one where the primary control of the numbers of senior medical staff was not within the ambit of the Department of Health.

FITZGERALD REPORT

The Committee, which met for the first time in November 1967 and reported in June 1968, saw the major defects in the acute hospital sector as:

(1) There are altogether 169 separate hospitals (with 20,840 beds) providing acute medical, surgical and maternity services. Most of them are inadequately staffed and equipped... Inadequate operating theatres, out-patient laboratory and radiological facilities are keeping patients in hospital longer than necessary.... As we shall show later, the requirements of a modern hospital service have become so complex that we can only meet them by a radical re-organisation of our hospital system involving, inter alia, a considerable reduction in the number of centres providing acute treatment.

(2) Another significant defect in the present hospital system is the lack of co-ordination between the various hospital authorities and the absence of a planned organisation of services... the need remains to achieve on a grander basis a planned and co-ordinated hospital organisation embracing both public authority and voluntary hospitals, while, at the same time, preserving and spreading the best features of the voluntary hospital.[5]

The Committee proposed a re-organisation of hospitals based on the following criteria:

(1) General Hospital - of not less than 300 beds with the minimum staffing level of two pathologists, two radiologists, three physicians, three

surgeons, two obstetricians-gynaecologists, three anaesthetists. It recommended that twelve such hospitals be established (see map for location).

(2) Regional Hospital - with at least 600 beds (and depending on the population to be served) and as many as 1,000 beds. Each specialist department to be staffed with at least two consultants. The organisational requirement was for three hospital regions (based on the experience of countries such as Scotland) sited on the medical schools and regional hospitals in Dublin (two), and one each in Cork and Galway.[6]

District hospitals, of which there were fifty-three comprising 1,925 beds, were to become District Nursing Homes staffed by general practitioners. County hospitals, all of whom had less than 200 beds and which were staffed, in the main, by a surgeon, a physician and part-time by a radiologist and anaesthetist, were to become Community Health Centres providing "in-patient services similar to that already suggested for District Nursing Homes (normal maternity, convalescents from the main hospitals and some geriatric services), but backed by somewhat increased diagnostic facilities and a more comprehensive consultant out-patient organisation"[7].

As to the timing of its recommendations, the Committee considered that all its major changes should be implemented by 1980. It viewed a single consultant organisation (involving both public and voluntary hospitals) as an essential prerequisite of its recommendations. It saw a reduction in the number of acute hospital beds made possible by "more suitable patient selection, more efficient bed utilisation, better out-patient services, improved transport services and the provision of hostel accommodation"[8]. The Committee acknowledged that its recommendations would require a modification of many recently-constructed hospitals but it viewed a decision to close them as a "cutting of our losses". (The public capital budget on hospital development in the period 1958-1968 was some £15.5

million). It was confident in its assertion that "the principles which have guided us have long been accepted in international medicine; they are recognised in all developed countries"[9].

To administer the proposed hospital system, the Committee recommended the establishment of a Consultants Establishment Board to "co-ordinate consultant appointments and to approve the creation of necessary new consultant posts". The Board should be reliant "largely on the advice and knowledge of its technical members" (medical consultants) who should have a two-thirds majority. Regional Hospital Boards should be established to have "responsibility for the general policy and supervision of the hospital services in their regions. The Boards would have as much independence as was practicable and would be financed on a block grant negotiated with the Department of Health". Hospital Management Committees would be established to run the hospitals. In the case of voluntary hospitals, "the lay board or religious community or combinations of these, as the case may be, would be, as at present, the management authority". Each regional and general hospital should "eventually employ a highly trained and experienced Administrator"[10].

The technocratic intent of Regional Hospital Boards, which were essential to the realisation of the Fitzgerald Committee's aims, were quickly blunted by the *real politik* of the Regional Health Boards. Indeed, as Chapter Four shows, the Hospital Boards were not promoted by the Department of Health nor supported by the newly-appointed Chief Executive Officers. Hospital planning, predicated on a national scale with supra-regional control, became the domain of local interests. Thus, while the prospective organisational controls were not made operational, the resourcing of hospitals continued apace.

CRITERIA FOR BED ALLOCATION

In crude terms, Ireland in 1968 had 7.2 acute beds per thousand of population, and Fitzgerald compared this with the situation in other countries (Table 2.1) and drew particular attention to the Irish position relative to England, Scotland and Northern Ireland. Defining "acute" more accurately to reflect the real case-mix of the hospitals, it calculated that Ireland had some 14,000 beds, a ratio of 4.9 per thousand of population. While it considered that a reduction in this figure was possible (dependent on the implementation of its strategic recommendations for General and Regional Hospitals), "we do not think it possible, due to the lack of precise information on the use of Irish hospitals, to give the exact level at which our bed provision should lie"[11]. Using the Scottish norm of 3.4 beds as a guide, the Committee calculated Irish acute bed requirements as in Table 2.2.

In 1986, the Department of Health reported that "in-patient acute care is provided in 152 hospitals which had a bed complement of 18,857 in 1984"[13]. While the 1986 publication does not provide comparative European data, the relevant 1984 publication citing Eurostat figures, is shown in Table 2.3.

PAST AS PORTENT

The Health Act, 1970, did not significantly alter the functions of the Department of Health which was established in 1947. These were outlined in a 1947 White Paper as follows: "the administration and business relating to the preparation, effective carrying out and co-ordination of measures conducive to the health of the people including, in particular, measures for

* the prevention and cure of disease;
* the treatment and cure of persons suffering from physical defects or mental illness;
* the regulation and control of the training and registration of persons for health services;
* control over the appointment and conditions of services of appropriate local officers;
* the initiation and direction of research;
* ensuring that impure or contaminated food is not marketed and that adequate nutritive standards obtain in essential foodstuffs;

*   the control of proprietary medical and toilet
      preparations;
*   the registration of births, deaths and marriages;
      and
*   the collection, preparation, publication and
      dissemination of information and statistics
      relating to health"[14].

In 1969, current public expenditure on health was some £52 million. Figure 2.1 sets out the ten-year trend for the years 1960-1970. Between 1968 and 1972 (at constant 1968 prices), current expenditure rose from £49.3 million to £72.5 million, an increase of some 47%.   In the same period, gross national product at constant prices is estimated to have increased by 13.9%.   Acute hospitals accounted for some 45% of this current expenditure[15].

The Health Act, 1970, did not introduce any significant extension in medical services.   Its justification lay in the re-organisation of existing services, the regionalisation of service-delivery and the introduction of a 'choice-of-doctor' scheme to replace the existing dispensary system.   The rationale for change, as expressed by the Minister for Health in 1969 on the introduction of the legislation "lay in the fact of the State's increasing financial commitment to the health services.   The government, by the White Paper, committed themselves to acceptance that the cost of specific further extensions of the services should not be met in any proportion by the local (authority) rates"[16].   The administrative machinery proposed for the hospital sector (regional boards) would ensure, he continued "a more efficient and effective service and a better return for the money we are spending.   Obviously, this must necessarily involve a willingness on the part of all hospital authorities to accept a planned and rational approach towards future organisation and development of the service"[17].   On the central issue of control of hospitals, the Minister (and his Department) compromised the Fitzgerald proposals for a separate and distinct regional-based hospital management system: "Section 40

(Section 41 of the 1970 Act) represents a compromise between what consultants might regard as the best form of administration for the hospital services and what government think public representatives at national and local level would accept for these purposes. Like most compromises, it will not fully satisfy everybody"[18].

Maynard, in an assessment made in 1975 of the re-organised Irish health-care system, observed: "the role of central government has changed into one of financing, supervising and monitoring. It is impossible to see how well this system will perform. No doubt some problems will arise. The obvious candidates for this role are the hospital system and the provision of complementary local authority welfare service...."[19].

The Health Act, 1970, is a very lengthy piece of legislation comprising some five parts with eighty-six distinct sections and three schedules of forty-two sections. Yet, many of the Act's provisions and the actual detail of the proposed re-organisation were not specified. The use of Ministerial Orders and Regulations (a technical device to give expression to legislative change) was widespread and covered such matters as the number and geographic area of the proposed health boards (Section 5.3), local advisory committees (Section 7.1), the establishment of Comhairle na nOspideal (Section 41.1(a)) and the setting up of regional hospital boards (Section 41.2(a)). Ministerial Orders and Regulations, while subject to Dail approval, do not receive the same scrutiny as legislative Bills. Indeed, the opposition at the time remarked: "We reject the Bill because it gives excessive power to the central government (and) The Bill is a mass of proposals set down in general terms to be implemented later by Ministerial regulations"[20]. The lack of specificity of the legislation was deliberate. The Health Act "deliberately departed from the tradition of detailed legislative provision and was 'followed up' by circulars and memoranda from the Department to the Health Boards outlining the intent and operation of health service policy provision"[21]. That is, the Department of Health saw itself exercising control as an administrative process and did not see the need for control to be embedded specifically in the legislation. Indeed, as Chapter Four shows, the Health Act 1970 was, in certain respects, a weaker instrument for hospital control than the 1953 legislation.

ADMINISTRATIVE CONTROL

If control was to be exercised through an administrative or managerial process, as opposed to legislative review or national standards, how was it to be expressed in the new organisational arrangements? It should be remembered that at approximately the same time as Ireland was pursuing an administrative-based strategy other European countries were taking a decidedly different route and incorporating key elements of control in legislation. In Ireland, the strategy was described as "more emphasis will be placed on control by way of general guidelines, directives, coupled with budgetary controls, in place of many of the individual approvals called for in the past"[22]. The idea of the Department of Health as the policy centre for the health services was in line with the 1969 Report of the Public Services Organisation Review Group (PSORG) which reported on the general organisation of the Irish Civil Service. PSORG saw policy creation and advice residing in central government departments whose senior officals' task was to advise the Minister (the Aireacht). Executive or line activities, the day-to-day running of services, were to be delegated to officials and agencies. Indeed, the Department of Health was the first department to be restructured on the PSORG model; Figure 1.1 outlines the proposed implementation in 1972. The data presented in this study shows how the technocratic assumptions of the PSORG model were vitiated by subsequent political decision-making in the Irish health services. It also demonstrates how the Irish model, unlike its European counterparts, was never adopted in legislation. One had, therefore, an extremely fragile system of control which was unlikely to be effective in achieving objectives which themselves were not clearly specified in legislation. The regionalisation of health-care services, the setting up of executive agencies such as the Health Boards and the adoption of 'staff-line' relationships in administrative management were all new and untried innovations in 1970. Based in part on a Scandanavian model of administration, the PSORG proposals represented a departure from the client-based system of political-administrative relationships in Ireland and they were never given legislative effect. In 1979, the PSORG recommendations were extended by government decision, to all departments. They were never reviewed, however, to ensure their effectiveness[24]. Indeed, a White Paper in 1985 on the Public Service stated that the staff units centralised decision-making and were not supportive of line managers. The White Paper also recommended that the division of administrators and professional grades into 'watertight grades' be abolished[25]. The divide between professional and administrative staff in the health service is explored in Chapters Five and Six. Thus, the re-organisation of health-care delivery was entrusted to a new administrative system, on a regional basis, that was unique in terms of service administration in Ireland. While other government departments had 'regions' for services delivery, the Health Boards were a unique combination of executive agency and public representation that had no parallel in Irish administration[26]. A central feature of the system was that 'policy' was to reside with the Department of Health and it was to be an administrative process, not a legislative one in terms of specification of standards or review of performance. The propositions and data in the following chapters are designed to test the efficacy of this system.

Indeed, so untried were the new arrangements that the Department of Health engaged McKinsey & Company to advise it on the actual implementation of the legislation, insofar as the operation and management of the Health Boards were concerned[27]. McKinsey & Company described the principles underlying their recommendations as follows:

1.   Professional and administrative responsibility

should be integrated at the various management levels to ensure that professional and administrative requirements and priorities are reconciled at an early stage in planning and implementation.

2. Management at each level should have reporting to it the necessary professional and administrative staff to deliver the appropriate mix of treatment, care and services for the target groups.

3. At each level, the management task of planning and controlling the delivery of health-care should not be too large for one individual, with the appropriate staff, to handle.[28]

The details of the McKinsey recommendations are examined in Chapters Five and Six.

UNRESOLVED ISSUES

The Health Act 1970, presaging as it did a major organisational change in health service delivery, was enacted without agreement with the medical and administrative profession on some basic 'rules of the game'. These were: a) basis of remuneration for general practitioners; b) nature of the control function in respect of voluntary hospitals; c) remuneration and control of voluntary hospital medical consultants, and d) performance measurement within the new regional structure. Here the regulation was not merely technical in nature; the medical consultants and the voluntary hospital system comprised some fifty percent of acute hospital beds in the country. The pressure on the Minister for Health and his Department was in 1969 and 1970 to get the legislation passed as 'health' was an important theme of the recent general election. The momentum was for the instigation of change, little regard was had to the imperative of control. As a Department of Finance official remarked "the Health Boards were set up to expand services"; their control, either monetary or professional, was not seen as an issue at the time[29].

In respect of the control of voluntary hospitals, which were funded almost entirely by the State but managed privately, the Minister for Health issued the following statement in 1971:

1. In Dail Eireann on the 26 March, 1969, the then Minister for Health referring to certain voluntary institutions (including hospitals) stated that there was no question arising under the Health Bill proposed at that time (now the Health Act, 1970) which would affect 'the ownership, operation or control' of such institutions. In the event, the Health Act, 1970, as enacted does not take from the proprietors of a voluntary hospital their rights of ownership, operation, or control of the hospital.

2. The Minister for Health, with the approval of the Government, wishes to make it clear that he accepts, as a principle, that the ownership of a voluntary hospital, as in the case of any other private ownership, of itself confers on the proprietors a basic measure of control over the hospitals' affairs, and that this basic measure of control should not be so reduced or diluted that the ownership itself ceases to be significant.

3. The Minister further wishes to make it clear that, taking due account of such system of financial control as may be settled between him and the voluntary hospitals, the basic measure of proprietary control by the competent authority of the hospital, referred to in the previous paragraph, includes, **inter alia,** the following:

    (a) the effective day-to-day administration and management of the hospital;

    (b) the effective day-to-day control of all hospital staff - medical and other;

    (c) the selection, appointment, remuneration

and discharage of staff, other than staff referred to at (d) below, subject to the approval, as now, in relation to numbers, remuneration and hours of duty of the Hospitals Commission and, later, the appropriate regional hospital board when established;

(d) the selection, appointment (or acceptance of assignment from the appropriate regional hospital board when established), remuneration and discharge of consultant medical and other senior medical and senior associated (for example, biochemist) staff who come within the functions of Comhairle na nOspideal (when established) subject to:

   (i) approval of Comhairle na nOspideal in regard to numbers and types;

   (ii) the operation of a method of selection introduced under the provisions of Section 41(1)(v) of the Health Act, 1970, on the understanding that the procedure would reserve to the competent authority in a voluntary hospital the right to refuse, for reasonable cause assigned, to accept the person selected, and

   (iii) approval of the Hospitals Commission or the appropriate regional hospital board when established in regard to remuneration.[30]

The efforts of successive administrations and the decisions of Comhairle na nOspideal did not result in a co-ordinated hospital policy up to 1987. How serious a failure this actually was is examined in Chapter Seven. Since the Voluntary Hospitals (in the main located in Dublin) received their budget allocation direct from the Department of Health, one Chief Executive Officer of a Health Board has written (in 1986): "some 30 percent of the health services' financial resources are allocated directly by the Department of Health to public voluntary hospitals and mental handicap organisations over which the Health Boards do not exercise any control.... The question to be answered is not if efforts to rationalise the hospital network in this country and to apply common standards of scrutiny should be pursued but rather if we, as a country, can afford not to confront these issues soon"[31].

ACCOUNTABILITY AND EFFECTIVENESS IN HEALTH CARE

As Hallas has noted, a direct consequence of the pursuit of cost efficiency is the greatly increased tendency to use overt and covert rationing of resources. Indeed, if acceptability is a criterion that is valued in any change in a health-care system, the following problem emerges: "the excitement engendered at the top of the organisation arises from redefining ways of doing things; it is "the challenge of change". At lower levels... this excitement is transmuted into sullen resentment about possible changes in the **status quo**.[32] Gray and Jenkins remark, in the context of State intervention that "the central issue is, therefore, however desirable change might appear or however clearly its logic might be stated by the centre of government, its implementation is frequently problematic rather than automatic"[33]. In the public perception, and in particular the viewpoint of control agencies such as the Department of Finance and Health, effective health-care has come to mean "health-care that is cost effective" and the rationale for the pursuit of effectiveness is that of cost containment. There is nothing wrong with such a definition of effectiveness as long as the major players in the system, i.e. patients, doctors and health-care workers, agree on the definition; the divergent viewpoints on this issue are described in later chapters. It is clear, however, that in Ireland, lacking a legislative statement of health-care objectives, there was no agreement on the nature of the effectiveness debate and the subsequent constraint on expenditure was accomplished by centralised decisions that ignored legitimate local or regional interests.

Closely related to the effectiveness debate is the nature of accountability in health-care services and the relative competing strengths of professional independence and public accountability. Oliver Wendell Holmes observed that "medicine, professedly founded on observation, is as sensitive to outside influences, political, religious, philosophical, imaginative, as is the barometer to the changes in atmospheric density"[34]. Less prosaically, the Medical Council of Ireland states that "doctors must be allowed an independence of thought, judgement and action if they are to be allowed to carry out their essential functions.... Society allows the doctor many privileges and with each of these goes responsibilities. If these privileges are used without a due sense of responsibility, there can be little surprise if a climate of public opinion develops in favour of limiting professional freedom"[35]. Dissatisfaction with traditional forms of control and regulation, either because it has proved ineffective or because the regulatory agency was "captured" by the personnel it was designed to control, has led to the search for more appropriate forms of control. The health-care system in Ireland, as in other countries, is a complex one. To the extent that politicians and civil servants think of control it usually is expressed in new administrative arrangements or structural change. Other European countries, by contrast, look first to the legislative basis of their health-care systems as this is their starting point for an effective control system. In Ireland, legislation is not seen as the basis for control and great reliance is placed on administrative compliance. This study demonstrates that such a strategy, in the absence of legislative policy on health-care objectives, is not a success. Control in Ireland is seen as requiring broad national policy objectives and it is the responsibility of the Health Boards and acute hospitals to implement the stated policies. This is not a model that would be recognised as effective in other modern European systems of health-care.

CONCLUSION

The 1966 White Paper and the Health Act 1970 did not advert to the principles on which the health services were to be re-organised. Finance, growing dissatisfaction with the organisation of primary-based medicine, and a desire to upgrade Irish standards to international levels were the dominant themes. Pragmatism was the leitmotiv of the time, and the only guiding statement as to the philosophy of the health services was the Minister's remark in the Dail that: "the Government did not accept the proposition that the State had a duty to provide unconditionally all medical, dental and other health services free of cost for everyone without regard to individual need or circumstances. On the other hand, no service is designed so that a person must show dire want before he can avail himself of it"[36]. This was written into legislation by the way of the term 'eligible' patient, and its usefulness as a strategy for hospital care is examined in Chapter Four. It is sufficient to note here that while health services were not to be free to all, the resultant measurement system did not specifically monitor the delivery of hospital services to the 'eligible' sector of the population.

The re-organisation in 1970 was a large and complex undertaking - a new regional structure of management was established, new regulatory agencies were set up, primary care was recast, and an upgrading and rationalisation of hospitals was contemplated. Control was to be an administrative-based process and it was viewed in a functional way - that is, it was for administrators to concern themselves with the actual detail, and no specific legislative guidelines were enacted. Given the assumption that health-care policy could be based on such a framework, how well did the endeavour fare? The following chapters explore the relationship between health-care policy and implementation in a comparative examination of the arrangements made by other European countries.

DISTRIBUTION OF PROPOSED REGIONAL AND GENERAL HOSPITALS

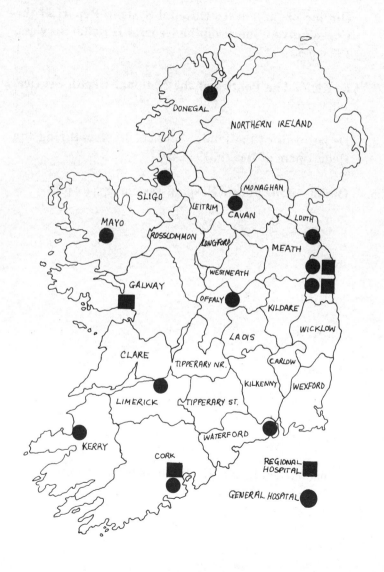

FOOTNOTES

1. R. Barrington, **Health, Medicine and Politics in Ireland 1900-1970,** 1987, p.261.

2. **Outline of the Future Hospital System, Report of the Consultative Council on the General Hospital Services,** 1968, p.5.

3. R. Klein, **The Politics of the National Health Service,** 1983, p.64.

4. Department of the Public Service, **Restructuring the Department of Health,** 1973, p.44.

5. **Outline of the Future Hospital System,** op.cit., p.17.

6. Ibid, pp.23-28.

7. Ibid, p.31.

8. Ibid, p.40.

9. Ibid, p.36.

10. Ibid, p.46.

11. Ibid, p.52.

12. Ibid, p.54.

13. Department of Health, **Health Statistics 1986,** p.52.

14. **Restructuring the Department of Health,** op.cit., p.11.

15. Ibid, p.4, facing p.10.

16. **Dail Debates,** Vol. 239, Column 1646.

17. Ibid, Columns 1649-1650.

18. Ibid, Column 1660.

19. A. Maynard, **Health Care in the European Community,** 1975, p.230.

20. **Dail Debates,** Vol. 239, Columns 1660 and 1691.

21. Note of Meeting with former Secretary, Department of Health, on 1 July 1987.

22. B. Hensey, **The Health Services of Ireland,** (2nd ed.), 1975 p.44.

23. **Restructuring the Department of Health,** op.cit., Exhibit 11, facing p.42.

24. See **Reports of the Public Service Advisory Council.**

25. Department of the Public Service, **Serving the Country Better - A White Paper on the Public Service,** 1985, p.17.

26. While other departments have geographic 'service' regions, these do not entail executive or managerial devolution of functions.

27. Department of Health, **Towards Better Health Care: Management in the Health Boards,** Vol. 11, 1970, Appendix A-1 and A-2. McKinsey & Company had the following terms of reference:

    The Department asked us to recommend answers to four main groups of questions that related to the setting up of the new Health Boards. These questions were:

1. **How should the Boards themselves conduct their affairs?**
   - What decisions should they make and what decisions should they delegate to their officers?
   - What committees should they have, in addition to the local committees set up under statute?

The Department did not ask us to make recommendations on the other new statutory bodies (the Comhairle na nOspideal, the Regional Hospital Boards and the local committees), but it was understood that we would have to consider the Board's relationships with these bodies, so that we could define the Board's own role clearly.

2. **What guidelines should be given concerning officers of the Boards?**
   - What should be the CEO's terms of reference?
   - What other senior officers should the Boards have, and should their numbers and functions vary among large and small boards?
   - What criteria should be used for recruiting and selecting these officers?

3. **What local offices would be needed?**
   - Should existing local offices (e.g. at county level) be kept open?
   - If so, what functions should these offices have?

4. **What further steps would be required after November 1?**

Since the deadline for the first report was very tight (only two months after the full-time start of the study), the Department recognised that much would have to be done after November 1 to make the new organisation effective. This task would involve two main areas, namely:

- What would have to be done to implement the organisational recommendations before April 1?

- How could a practical management information and budgeting system be developed and introduced to meet the Board's decision-making requirements?

These four groups of questions then are the ones we set out to investigate and on which we promised to advise the Department. We also agreed that the approach taken to the assignment should be broad rather than narrow, and should take into account the particular needs and opportunities of the health services in Ireland.

28. Ibid, Vol. iv, p.(i)

29. Personal communication, Department of Finance, 20 May 1987.

30. **Dail Debates,** Vol. 255, 22 July 1971, Columns 2363-2365.

31. D.J. Doherty, "Rationalising Hospital Services", p.25, in **Seirbhis Phoibli,** Vo7, No. 1, March 1986.

32. J. Hallas, "Acceptability in an Effectiveness and Efficiency Climate", p.101 in A. Long and S. Harrison (ed), **Health Services Performance,** 1985.

33. A. Grey and W.I. Jenkins, **Administrative Politics in British Government,** 1985, p.221.

34. Oliver W. Holmes, **Medical Essays,** 1883.

35. The Medical Council, **A Guide to Ethical Conduct and Behaviour and to Fitness to Practice,** 1984, p.13.

36. **Dail Debates,** Vol. 239, Columns 1636.

CHAPTER THREE

The Challenge of Control

Health-care policies are, as we have seen, a complex mix of financial, social and administrative arrangements which give rise to particular challenges for government and, indeed, the patient. A central view of the present study is that research in the area of publicly-funded health-care poses important organisational and human questions and that a management approach grounded in an accepted and documented corporate strategy model provides a perspective that allows for a serious exploration of the issues involved. The question relates to the organisational and human factors in the provision of a public service, as distinct from the target or ostensible purpose of that service. In relation to control systems, the provision of a public service, such as health, can be treated by much the same analytical techniques as the activities of a business enterprise, allowing that one is 'not-for-profit' and the other is 'for-profit'. Back of these analytical techniques is the view of the individual in a social context most appropriately expressed by the Rabbi Hillel: "If I am not for myself, then who is for me? And if I am not for others, then who am I? And if not now, then when?" Management is about people in organisations and about ways to resolve the conflicting claims of individual self-achievement and of social conscience. In an ultimate sense, the present study is about how professional people behave in an organisation which has resources available but not a proper control system, and is, therefore, about a moral problem. But the study does have immediate practical importance. The primary difficulty in assessing investment in health care is the uncertainty as to its likely outcome and the relationship between health-care expenditure and improvement in health status. This uncertainty is increased when, as in Ireland, there is no information available on the activities of professionals in the health services. The highly contingent nature of health-care investment requires, therefore, clear strategic objectives that will focus the investment decision and encourage professional compliance through relevant performance assessment. It is clear that Ireland's strategic policy, which is evaluated in Chapter Four, does not meet these criteria. The present chapter describes a framework for the assessment of health-care investment strategy which shows that it requires more than the decision to allocate resources for the modernising of Irish health-care facilities.

In the literature on the organisation of health-care systems, the central focus is on the administrative or managerial arrangements. The National Health Service (NHS) in the United Kingdom is regarded as the most effective in terms of cost containment and it has attracted envious comment from some United States observers. Yet, while the NHS may be satisfactory from a resource-use perspective, it has been criticised by some observers who contend that it restricts the choice of the consumer and, hence, distorts the 'market for health-care'; Green's work at the Institute for Economic Affairs is an example of such commentary[1]. The model used in this research, drawing as it does on the Business Policy perspective, incorporates the financial and organisational stance of earlier research. In addition, its focus on resource allocation at each level in the system (national, regional and hospital) allows one to survey the practical implementation of national health-care objectives. It, therefore, meets the requirement of addressing a major practical problem in contemporary policy studies.

The model also incorporates one of the central dilemmas that faces the national planner of health-care policy. Eckstein puts it thus: "all of this illustrates one of the fundamental dilemmas of the planning process: the need to operate either without standards of calculation or with over-standardised or over-simplified procedures. In a situation which practically precludes fully rational behaviour, planners try to create a set of conditions in which a high degree of calculated decision-making is possible, even if those conditions are irrelevant to, or impede, the achievement of their goals. They try to maximise the conditions of the formally rational at the expense of substantively rational behaviour; in short, they tend to re-create in the planned system the very faults of the spontaneous system"[2]. He goes on to attribute the tendency of centralisation to this dilemma.

The planning of health-care, its regulation and management, is a complex activity. For Government, choice must be exercised between the role assigned to central planning and the autonomy allowed to individuals and local administration. The system incorporates redistributive transfer payments via national medical insurance schemes, complex technologies for diagnostic treatment, together with an institutional mix of public and private. Measurement and information systems must attend to this diversity and the hospital sector has to be managed within the context of a multi-unit organisational structure. The research propositions in this study allows one to examine this diversity and they are grounded within a well-documented control paradigm that takes account of the specific characteristics of medical care and hospital administration.

RESEARCH MODEL

A recent review of international comparative research in health-care observed that "in general, it can be said that the majority of the studies are descriptive. There is usually no clear model for analysis, even in those studies that in other respects could be classified as analytical. Models and theories are seldom dealt with".[3] This chapter presents a model for discussion and compares it with other models and approaches that have been utilised in health-care research. A central feature of this study is the emphasis on the inter-relationship between national policies and their practical implementation. The model, which was developed by Bruce Scott in his DBA thesis, 'An Open System Model of the Firm' was later applied in a study of industrial planning in France, asserts that: 1) any organisation relates to its environment via a strategy for advancing its interests as it perceives these interests; 2) the interests of the various subunits of an organisation often differ from those of the organisation as a whole, and 3) thus the central or general headquarters of the organisation must bring continuous influence to bear on the subunits in order to motivate them to act in conformity with the general or shared interests of the organisation[4]. Scott went on to assert that the most important forms of influence are: the ability to allocate resources, to measure and reward performance, and to formulate policy limits or "rules of the game".

The present study examines the validity of the following set of propositions:

1. The Irish health-care system has developed as a government-financed activity, yet it has operated without a statement of mission.

2. Because of the lack of an objective statement of the mission of the Irish health-care system, the general hospital segment, either public or voluntary, has no defined role, and no rational system of resource allocation.

3. Because the general hospital segment has no defined role, and no rational system of resource allocation, its control system has developed no objective and measurable norms:

   (a) Resource allocation is highly centralised in Dublin and the system lacks responsiveness to local health needs in the remainder of Ireland;

   (b) the professionals within hospitals have created slack and captured that slack for their own benefit; and

   (c) there is no impetus to clarify the mission of the health-care system as a whole.

The propositions are tested using data from a number of sources. First, the legislative basis of Irish health-care is examined to see what guidelines or policy it contains that would assist health-care managers and medical personnel in their work. Second, data on health-care spending and resource allocation for Ireland and other European countries is examined and the relationship between programme objectives and their effectiveness explored. Third, an examination of hospital budgetting, both public sector and voluntary, to test the validity of the proposition on centralisation of resource allocation. Fourth, the study utilises data from interviews with health-care managers and medical personnel in Ireland and in Sweden and the Netherlands to give the experience of people directly involved in the day-to-day task of health-care delivery. The research is of the nature where the challenge is to document propositions that are plausible (but may still not be true) - as distinct from research aimed to yield propositions that are novel and unexpected.

RESEARCH FOCUS

It is proposed that the Irish acute hospital sector be considered analogous to a subunit which has objectives and resources that contribute to the overall mission of Irish health-care policy. The role for the State, or the Department of Health, in this model, is to ensure, through the means of influence available to it, that the hospital sector is effectively contributing to national health-care objectives. A review of the hospital sector can then be examined in the context of a "whole-part" relationship which would evaluate its contribution to overall health policy objectives. The model would also assist in the definition of the role of the acute hospital **relative** to other levels of the health-care delivery system.

The specific orientation of the research is the relationship between the existing control system in the hospital sector and its contribution to the evaluation of strategic policy in the health area. The reasons for this orientation are as follows:

1.   Hospital costs are a significant part of overall health-care costs and these costs have been targetted by the Department of Health as the sector where a redistribution of resources should take place.

2.   The proposed shift to primary, community-based, health-care will have significant resource implications for the hospital sector and any change in funding should be linked to the control system that evaluates performance; otherwise, managers and physicians will not understand (or contribute to) the revised "rules of the game".

3. To consider whether the existing control system can effectively contribute to the proposed changes in the health-care system.

COMPARATIVE FOCUS

It should be noted that control is not about the setting of standards or norms. It is about the maintaining of norms, the following of patterns and rules once these have been laid down. Thus, while there have been proposals made to lessen the dominant role of hospitals in health services, with greater emphasis on primary/community care, the strategic choice determining the overall system has remained. That is, Ireland is to have internationally accepted standards and norms of health-care comparable to more advanced economies than our own. The central proposition of this strategy may be characterised as follows:

Acceptance of International _____ Units of
    Standards and Norms   Resources

A more modest and realistic approach would be to link our economic performance to the achievement of a comparative share of international norms and standards. The central proposition may be characterised as follows:

Agreed units of resources _____ Comparative Share of
    for the system   international standards

The study examines how other countries, i.e. Sweden and the Netherlands, evaluate and control hospital performance in the context of overall health policy and how these performance measurements are linked to the strategic health-care policy of these countries. The study also examines whether there is a linkage between control and the resource allocation model used to fund hospital services. That is, the study seeks to validate the proposition that agreement is required on the role of the hospital, within the health-care delivery system, prior to any objective measurement of its performance, and that the resource allocation process should be congruent with the stated goal of the hospital sector.

The research model and methodology concentrates on the issue of health policy and objectives within the context of how the State can use the means of influence available to it to achieve its stated policy objectives. The relationship between hospital performance measurement and resource allocation is considered to be an outcome of a prior agreement/consensus on what the role of the hospital is within the health-care delivery system. If this relationship is not validated by the data, then it will have revealed important issues of control that will have to be tackled within the Irish policy system.

The emphasis on the 'mission' of the health-care system, and the role of the hospital sector relative to it, is designed to concentrate attention on the basic strategy or objective that the State adopted in Ireland towards health-care investment. The advantage of a comparative focus, and the research propositions, is that one can examine how other countries have tackled the problems of health-care policy and service delivery. To address service provision only would be to deflect attention to operational issues and ignore the strategy underlying investment decisions. It would not assist in the clarification of aims and objectives ('mission') and it would provide no comparative focus on how other countries have modified and strengthened their control systems, in the face of similar economic, social and political challenge.

CONTROL AND MEDICAL CARE MARKETS

Child offers the following description: "Control within an organisation is a process whereby management and other groups are able to initiate and regulate the conduct of activities so that the results accord with the goals and expectations held by these groups. Control, in other words, is aimed at ensuring that a predictable level and type of performance is attained and maintained"[5].

The essential characteristic of control is the gathering of information, its diffusion through the organisation as the basis for consensual decision-making in the review of agreed targets and performance. A central thesis of this study is that the Irish publicly-financed health-care system does not possess such a control system.

Management control in an organisation, public or private, for profit or not-for-profit, has to do with the measurement of the organisation's achievement and the assembly of information on its performance relative to its aims and objectives. The challenge to management in a medical care system is a profound one when the incidence of uncertainty is so pervasive. This uncertainty takes many forms. The most basic is the efficacy of the many modes of treatment that are available due to the rapid technological and therapeutic advances in medical science and practice. Closely associated with this phenomenon is the cost of the medical care provision and its allocation among the various parts of the system, i.e. primary, community and hospital. The financing of medical care and its allocation relative to other areas of social or economic expenditure is also made more difficult if the control system is unable to effectively regulate the activities of the individuals delivering the service. The advocacy of public or private provision of health-care does not, however, remove the challenge of control and regulation. As Battistella and Eastaugh remark in the context of hospital cost containment in the United States: "Among regulators, the service ethic is often derided as a synonym for soft-heartedness and weak-mindedness. Such disdain contributes to the surprise of regulators over the felicity with which hospital administrators manage to avoid the intent of quantitative controls"[6]. Thus, it is important that the professionals within the system and those charged with its management agree as to the objectives of the enterprise. One of the research's propositions is that the "Irish health-care system... has operated with an objective statement of its mission". The basis for this proposition is discussed in Chapter Four but it can now be seen that both the nature of the medical care market itself and the consensual basis of management control are important features of the proposition.

THE PROCESS OF CONTROL

Kenneth Arrow, in a study of the welfare economics of medical care compares the operation of the industry with the operation of competitive model, that is: "the flows of services that would be offered and purchased and the prices that would be paid for them if each individual in the market offered or purchased services at the going prices as if his decisions had no influence over them, and the going prices were such that the amounts of services which were available equalled the total amounts which other individuals were willing to purchase, with no imposed restrictions on supply or demand"[7]. He contended that the special problems of medical care can be explained as "adaptions to the existence of uncertainty in the incidence of disease and in the efficacy of treatment". The prevalance of uncertainty in medical care and the structural characteristics of the medical care market "are largely attempts to overcome the lack of optimality due to the non-marketability of the bearing of suitable risks and the imperfect marketability of information"[8].

The decision environment in medical care itself is uncertain. The management of uncertainty calls for a strategy of control that will take account of this phenomenon. The term 'judgemental strategy' has been used by Thompson to define decisions where cause-effect relationships are uncertain but where outcome preferences are clear. The following is his decision-matrix:

		Certainty	Uncertainty
Beliefs about cause/effect relations	Certain		
	Uncertain		

The management of health-care delivery systems can be seen as requiring a judgemental strategy. Thompson goes on to state the following proposition: "the more numerous the areas in which the organisation must rely on the judgemental decision strategy, the larger the dominant coalition"[9].

MEASUREMENT AND CONTROL IN COMPLEX ORGANISATIONS

If the primary criteria for investment is availability of resources, then in a period of restraint the question arises as to the maintenance of the quality of medical care. It will be shown in the next chapter that the Irish system did not develop norms and standards for service delivery and that the absence of a strategic legislative framework further complicates the process of evolving a purposeful statement of such norms.

Within the hospital system the task of measurement has usually been applied to the number of beds in the system and their cost implications. As Fokkens has remarked, "another, more prosaic, reason is that data on the utilisation of other facilities are scarcely available or accessible"[10]. Anthony and Herzlinger, in a study of control in non-profit organisations, discussed the tendency in health-care and hospital systems to concentrate on quantitative measures in the absence of information on quality. They offer a number of general propositions: 1) some measure of output is usually better than none; 2) use measures that can be repeated in a timely manner; 3) if feasible, tie output measures to expense measures; 4) don't give more credence to surrogates than is warranted[11].

The nature of measurement in the context of the research model can be summarised as follows: measurement must relate to the objectives (mission) of the organisation and complex organisations require multi-dimensional measures. The system of measurement must be understood by the people whose activities are being measured ("rules of the game"). A two-way flow of information is critical. The control system is itself rectificatory and not restorative and the model assumes that X resources buys Y units of service, and not that X units requires Y resources.

Management control and the efficacy of the control system is necessarily dependent on the nature and complexity of the organisation. The main features of a control system can be seen in the means of influence described by Scott and McArthur: these are, the ability to allocate resources, to establish and alter organisational structures, to reward and measure performance, and to formulate policy limits or "rules of the game". The size and/or the complexity of an organisation is an important variable when one is considering a control system. A health-care delivery system, either at national, regional or acute hospital level is a complex one and it, therefore, requires multi-dimensional controls to adequately assess its performance. For example, take the decision-making in the allocation and control of an acute general hospital with a budget of some £30 million. (The operational content of Irish hospital budgetting is set out in Chapter Five).

The hospital budget can be decided broadly along three dimensions. First, last year's budget can be taken and an increment (or decrement) given on the basis of this year's projected activity. Second, the budgets of similar hospitals (controlled for case-mix, technology and staffing) in Ireland or elsewhere can be examined to arrive at the budget. Third, the budget can be allocated on the basis of the overall cash allocation to the region in which the hospital is located so as to take account of priorities in the mode of service delivery; e.g., a priority to finance and encourage primary or non-residential or ambulatory care would result in a decrease or standstill in the hospital's budget. Except for the first case, and to some degree even there, the resource allocation system requires information across a broad range of activities and variables such as - demographic and epidemiological data, costs for case-mix and for staffing (to include fixed and variable costs), data on the efficacy of treatment (there may well be more efficacious and/or less costly procedures), data on projected asset-replacement and the cost of servicing such assets. In addition, management would require information on personnel and their performance and the plans/proposals of the medical personnel as to projected budgets. "Trade-offs" for achieving service targets and financial targets have also to be made.

Bower, in his study of the capital allocation decision, describes three major processes: "(a) the intellectual activities of perception, analysis and choice - 'decision-making'; (b) the social process of implementing formulated policies by means of organisational structure, systems of measurement and allocation, and systems of rewards and punishment; (c) the dynamic process of revising policy as changes in organisational resources and the environment change the context of the original policy problem"[12]. The three concepts central to the decision process he characterises as 'Definition, Impetus and Context'. Impetus is the essentially political process that motivates the resource allocating part of his model and it is discussed in Chapter Four. As already noted in Chapter Two, the link between plans and operations is problematic. So too is the linkage between the budgets of individual units (e.g. department in a hospital) or programmes and the overall objectives of the area (health board region, or hospital). That is, the sub-units can have plans or expenditures which, viewed in the context of the overall organisation, do not "add up".

Cyert and March explain this apparent contradition of conflicting aims and objectives: "the notion of attention focus suggests one reason why organisations are successful in surviving with a large set of unrationalised goals. They rarely see the conflicting objectives simultaneously... the organisation can remain viable by attending to the demands sequentially"[13]. The proposition that the Irish health-care system "lacks impetus to clarify its mission" is derived from the earlier propositions and the proposition of 'sequential attention to demands'.

CONCLUSION

The model and the propositions are concerned with the

relationship between the investment strategy of the organisation and the challenge posed by the environment to the realisation of this strategy.   The model embraces public and private provision of services and is not dependent on a unitary form of an administrative or measurement system.   Indeed, stressing as it does the complexity and diversity of organisational aims, the model mirrors the reality of national health-care systems, and together with a comparative focus, facilitates a study of health-care policy formulation that is grounded in the decision-making environment of modern economies.

The Irish health-care delivery system was substantially altered and revised in 1970.   New forms of administration, regional levels of management and regulatory agencies were established. The following chapters examine the assumptions, administrative and conceptual, underpinning this re-organisation and compares them to the responses of other European countries.   It will be demonstrated that Ireland was unique, not in the environment that it faced, but in the strategy it adopted to a shared European problem - the regulation and mangement of health-care policy and service delivery.

FOOTNOTES

1. D. Green, **Challenge to the NHS,** 1987 and **Which Doctor?,** 1985.

2. H. Eckstein, **The English Health Service,** 1964, p.278.

3. L. Van Atteveld, C. Broeders, R. Lopre "International Comparative Research in Health Care", pp.107-108, in **Health Policy,** No. 8, 1987.

4. J. McArthur, and B.R. Scott, **Industrial Planning in France,** 1969, p.112.

5. J. Child, **Organization,** 1984, p.136.

6. R. Battistella and S. Eastaugh, "Hospital Cost Containment", p.193 in A. Levin (ed), **Regulating Health Care: The Struggle for Control,** 1980.

7. K. Arrow, "Uncertainty and the Welfare Economics of Medical Care", p.13, in Cooper, H. and Cuyler, A. (ed) **Health Economics,** 1973.

8. Ibid, p.19.

9. J.D. Thompson, **Organizations in Action,** 1967, p.134.

10. O. Fokkens, "Hospital Planning - The Dilemma of the Average", p.125 in P. Lambert and F.H. Roger (eds) **Hospital Statistics in Europe,** 1982.

11. R. Anthony and R. Herzlinger, **Management Control in Non-Profit Organizations,** 1980, pp.242-243.

12. J. Bower, **Managing the Resource Allocation Process,** 1970, pp.54-64.

13. R.M. Cyert and J. March, **A Behavioural Theory of the Firm,** p.35.

CHAPTER FOUR

National Health Care Strategies

This chapter examines the validity of the proposition that the Irish health-care system has developed as a government-financed activity, yet it has operated without an objective statement of its mission. In the public sector, the role of the central civil service departments is to control the activities of its agencies through the 'means of influence' available to them. These include legislation, the administrative management system and the conditions of employment of their staff. The term 'mission' embraces the legislative basis of health-care policy, government decisions on service provision and the response of the civil service in the implementation of these policies.

'Mission' is an important concept in the analysis of social expenditure programmes and it can be viewed as similar to corporate strategy in the private sector where it is "a set of objectives... against which progress in the desired direction may be measured and a timed sequence of conditional moves for deploying skills and resources with a view to attaining one's objectives". It is clear from this study that other countries, confronted by similar challenges in health-care policy, have responded differently from Ireland and that their legislation is a central component of this response. Legislation is also important in the context of the policy for the re-orientation of health care provision towards preventive, community-based care as it is difficult to see how such a policy could be implemented without a legislative statement of its aims and objectives. The European countries examined in this study adapted and changed their legislation to take account of, and give effect to, changes in their health-care investment strategies.

Legislation in the public sector provides a framework for management control. The 1970 Health Act represented a departure from detailed provisions of control to one based on the administrative model of 'staff-line' relationships. The lack of specificity in the Irish legislation was not a problem as long as resources were available for the expansion of services. In the absence of norms for service delivery, the allocation of extra resources allowed for a build-up of 'slack' within the system. The rigid nature of the resource allocation system (described in the next chapter), both at national and regional level, resulted in disparity in service provision which was exacerbated by the absence of norms and standards in the legislation. Moreover, in a period of retrenchment, the administrative centre had to oversee cuts in services and they could not legitimise their action by reference to legislation which defined government policy. This situation marks Ireland as different from the other European countries who possess legislation which defines and describes consensual health-care objectives.

In 1972, the Minister for Health stated that "the setting up of the Health Boards and Regional Hospital Boards, the County Advisory Health Committees and Comhairle na nOspideal, represent the ultimate in developing a specific national service by decentralisation of executive services, by ensuring maximum communication down to county electoral level, while at the same time ensuring general national control at Ministerial and Oireachtas level"[1]. The data presented in this chapter describes a very different perspective from that of the 'centre' controlling a national health care service. The 'centre' lacked any clearly defined mission, unlike the Netherlands and Sweden, and government policy in the latter end of the 1970's treated health care as an arm of its economic renewal programme. The legislative basis of Irish health care, primarily concerned with administrative and organisational matters, did not provide a control mechanism which related expenditure to specific policy objectives. The common experience of Sweden and the Netherlands, countries very different in their funding and administrative systems, demonstrates the validity of the proposition that national health care policy requires a mission (or strategy) statement which is incorporated into legislation.

The analysis of government policy and the response of civil servants is treated from a 'public choice' perspective. As O'Mahony observes "the central insight of public choice theory is that politicians and civil servants have ends of their own, or that, in other words they are utility-maximizers like the rest of us. As such, they are "actors" within, rather than without, the socio-economic system"[2]. If, as in Ireland, legislation is weak, then administrative control is contingent on government adopting consistent policy aims for health-care delivery. This was not the case in Ireland throughout the 1970's and it seriously weakened the administrative centre's capacity for control. Health care was as much seen as an instrument of economic policy as it was an expression of the State's responsibility for the health of its population. The abandonment of the Fitzgerald proposals for hospital planning, the adoption of job-creation programmes in the health service and the consistent sanction of large supplementary estimates for health board and voluntary hospitals seriously weakened control in the system. This chapter describes these policy shifts and it argues that the absence of legislative expression of health care objectives in Ireland constitutes a serious technical and social barrier to change.

IRISH HEALTH-CARE LEGISLATION

The 1970 Health Act was primarily administrative in orientation and no new services were instituted under its provision. The Act did provide for a re-organised primary health service, with choice of practitioner to replace the old dispensary system. The Health Act 1947, which was the primary act promulgated under the newly-established Department of Health, was entitled: "An Act to make further and better provision in relation to the health of the people and to provide for the making of regulations by virtue of which certain changes may be made"[3]. The Health Act of 1953 extended and modified the 1947 Act and their effect was that "the County Councils, as health authority, administered all the health services (apart from the mental treatment service) in most parts of the country". In terms of a policy for service provision, the effect was described by a former Secretary of the Department of Health as "the policy which evolved from this period (1946-1960) and to which concrete expression was given in the Health Act 1963 can be summarised as providing for each class the services which the persons in it could not afford"[4].

The 1953 Health Act, in Section 14(2), described 'eligible'persons as "persons who are unable to provide by their own industry or other lawful means the medical, surgical, opthalmic, dental or aural treatment, or medicines, or medical, surgical or dental appliances necessary for themselves or their dependants"[5]. Barrington, in an analysis of the discussions and negotiations that took place prior to the passage of the 1954 Act, remarked in the context of these criteria that "the notion of access to all services on the basis of medical need alone gave way to complex eligibility criteria, largely based on income, varying from service to service"[6].

The 1970 Health Act modified these provisions as follows:

45   (1)   A person in either of the following categories shall have full eligibility for the services under this Part -

   (a)   adult persons unable without undue hardship to arrange general practitioner medical and surgical services for themselves and their dependants;

   (b)   dependants of the persons referred to in paragraph (a).

   (2)   In deciding whether or not a person comes within the category mentioned in subsection (1)(a), regard shall be had to the means of the spouse (if any) of that person in addition to the person's own means.

   (3)   The Minister may, with the consent of the Minister of Finance, by regulations specify a class or classes of persons who shall be deemed to be within the categories mentioned in subsection (1).

(4) A draft of regulations which it is proposed to make under this section shall be laid before each House of the Oireachtas and the regulations shall not be made until a resolution approving of the draft has been passed by each House.

(5) Section 5(5) of the Health Act, 1947, shall not apply to regulations under this section.

(6) References in this part to persons with full eligibility shall be construed as referring to persons in the categories mentioned in subsection (1) or deemed to be within those categories.

(7) Any person who is not in either of the categories mentioned in subsection (1) but who, in relation to a particular service which is available to persons with full eligibility, is considered by the chief executive officer of the appropriate health board to be unable, without undue hardship, to provide that service for himself or his dependants shall, in relation to that service, be deemed to be a person with full eligibility.[7]

Table 4.1 sets out the percentage of the population deemed fully 'eligible' under the legislation in 1985.

The strategy underlying the provision of health services was described by the Minister at the introduction of the 1970 Health Act as "the present government had not accepted the proposition that the State had a duty to provide unconditionally all medical, dental and other health services free of cost for everyone"[8]. In relation to the span or quality of services and their actual provision, however, the health acts are silent. The issue of service provision and its relationship to hospital services was tested in an action before the Irish Supreme Court in 1984. The Supreme Court held that the Minister for Health, under Section 38(2) of the 1970 Act, had acted **ultra vires** in directing a Health Board to discontinue certain in-patient services in a hospital, without holding a local inquiry. More important, from a policy perspective on service delivery is the **obiter dicta** of one Supreme Court Judge that "there is no definition of 'provide' either in the Act of 1947 or the Act of 1970. In my view, in its proper context in relation to a hospital, 'providing' a hospital is not confined to the supply of the structure in which the hospital is carried on. It would embrace the supply of all necessary equipment, both specialised and what might be called domestic, and all surgical, gynaecological, radiological, nursing, para-medical, and domestic personnel and services (and this list is not by any means exclusive). Under the rules of construction, statutes ought to be construed so as to carry out the objects sought to be accomplished by them, and a reasonable construction of a statute should, if possible, prevail. As stated earlier, the object of the Health Acts is to make further and better provision in relation to the health of the people"[9].

In describing the functions of the Health Boards, the Court held that they were (under Section 6 of the 1970 Act) "what may, generally, be described as the health functions formerly discharged by the local authorities in the particular region, together with such additional functions as were conferred by the Act"[11].

Section 6(1) and (2) of the Act states that:

(1) Subject to Section 17, a health board shall perform the functions conferred on it under this Act and any other functions which, immediately before its establishment were performed by a local authority (other than as a sanitary authority) in the functional area of the health board in relation to the operation of services provided under, or in connection with the administration of, the enactments specified in subsection (2).

(2) The enactments referred to in subsection (1) are -

    (a)   the Health Acts 1947 to 1966.

    (b)   The Mental Treatment Acts, 1945 to 1966.

    (c)   the Births and Deaths Registration Acts, 1863 to 1952.

    (d)   the Notification of Births Acts, 1907 to 1915.

(e)   the Act's relating to the registration of marriages.

(f)   the Sale of Food and Drugs Acts, 1875 to 1936.

(g)   Part 1 of the Children's Act, 1908, and Sections 2 and 3 of the 1957, Children (Amendment) Act, 1957.

(h)   the Rats and Mice (Destruction) Act, 1919.

(i)   the Blind Persons Act, 1920.

(j)   the State Lands (Workhouses) Act, 1930 and the State Lands (Workhouses) Act, 1962.

(k)   the Registration of Maternity Homes Act, 1934.

(l)   the Midwives Act, 1944, as amended by the Nurses Act, 1950.

(m)   the Adoption Acts, 1952 and 1964.

(n)   the Poisons Act, 1961.[11]

In legislative terms, therefore, there is no statement of what range or quality of service is required of the Health Boards. One Chief Executive Officer stated that the "Department of Health has no legislative basis for the setting of norms for service delivery at regional level"[12]. The actual day-to-day monitoring of service delivery is entrusted to the Health Boards, while the Department and Minister of Health had overall co-ordination and direction[13].

The Health Board system was an innovation in Irish administrative practice and the Irish legislation in 1970 departed from the existing administrative system for the provision of local services. In a review of hospital legislation in fifty-two countries, Bridgeman and Roemer state: "it is therefore clear that, whatever the degree of decentralisation, the tendency is to model the health system on that of the general administration"[14]. The Health Act 1970, with its regionalisation of service delivery, demonstrably did not pattern health delivery administration on the 'general administration'. One observer, who was a local elected representative, characterised it as follows: "imposed from the above, these bodies are distinguished by the number of disputes they generate at local level, precisely because they are not rooted in the popular will. They are expressions of administrative efficiency it is true, but are they expressions of political efficiency as well?"[15]. A Chief Executive Officer of a Health Board, reviewing the practical application of the process, described the mix to the author as follows: "a body which is so widely representative (and) we foolishly expect them to make cost-effective decisions"[16].

The competing claims of local politicians and economic efficiency, as envisaged by the Fitzgerald Report, were never resolved. Chapter Two discussed this tension and it argued that the resources sanctioned in the 1970's allowed for 'slack' in the system which ensured that the relationship between economic efficiency and local participation was never tested. With economic constraint in the 1980's, the issue is again at the heart of the agenda. The existing legislative and administrative system is, however, unable to resolve it.

The Regional Hospital Boards, set up under Section 41(2), had the following functions:

(a) to consider and keep under review the general organisation and development of in-patient and out-patient services in the hospitals administered by the Health Boards or by other bodies in their functional area which are engaged in the provision of services under the Act, with a view to promoting the organisation and development of these services in an efficient and satisfactory manner;

(b) to make such recommendations as it thinks fit arising from the consideration and review under para.(a) to the Minister, the Health Boards or any other body concerned;

(d) to advise the Minister on hospital policy insofar as it effects the functional area of the Board;

(h) to examine, to the extent determined by the Minister, the estimates of receipts and expenditure of the relevant Health Boards (insofar as they relate to hospital services) and other bodies administering in their functional area hospitals providing services under the Act and to make to the Minister any recommendations on such estimates as it thinks fit;

(i) to allocate to hospital projects (including projects for equipment) in its area the public capital funds made available by the Minister to the extent that such funds are not specifically allocated by the Minister for projects which, in his opinion are major projects;

(g) to govern the numbers and types of officers and employments (other than those referred to in Section 41(ii) b(i) of the Act) in such hospitals and except insofar as the Minister has the function, the removal of such officers.

The Boards never operated effectively; they were opposed by the Chief Executive Officers and they were not promoted actively by the Department of Health itself. The technocratic vision of the Fitzgerald Committee was blunted by the geographic and economic reality of the County Hospital system. Indeed, Comhairle na nOspideal was unable to fashion a hospital structure, in some measure, due to this reality (see Chapter Seven). The 'rules of the game' in legislative and administrative terms were clear; the various participants in the system (Health Boards, voluntary hospitals and health service professionals) were not to be subject to the proposed 'co-ordination'. It could well be that the original legislative intent was misguided or inappropriate, yet no new legislative change has been enacted since 1970. Indeed, the process has become even more an administrative-based one and it is argued on the basis of this study that it lacks legitimacy in the context of the experience of the other countries studied. It is also the case that administrative management was subject to the constraints of political policy and that the investment in hospitals and an increase in health-service personnel was regarded as a popular political policy. In this fashion, therefore, the administrative 'centre' of the Departments of Health and Finance were themselves unsure throughout much of this period what the 'rules of the game' were. The 'hands-off' approach pursued by the Department of Health in its budget allocation decisions in 1987 should be seen in this context; administrators were, to some degree, reluctant to assume responsibility for service curtailment decisions they regarded as the 'responsibility' of government. It also accounts, perhaps, for the expressions of political disquiet as to the 'top-heavy' bureaucracies of the Health Boards.

Legislation did not prescribe a strategy for health-care provision and government decisions on hospitals had the effect of resourcing a much larger physical base than that envisaged by Fitzgerald. It was also the case that the decisions of the Health Boards, because of their political composition, encouraged the trend to resource all hospitals rather than to concentrate on the larger units. This has led to a questioning of the value of the Health Board structure on the grounds of efficiency. It is, however, to misconstrue the real nature of the problem - that is, the lack of a formal strategy, expressed in legislation, which would govern the allocation of resources to the various programme areas. If government policy was expressed in appropriate legislation, as it is in the Netherlands and Sweden, then resource decisions would be consistent with such policy. It is also the case that such legislation would constrain the government's freedom to take politically-popular decisions at the expense of consistent policy on hospital provision.

DUTCH HEALTH-CARE LEGISLATION

The striking difference between health-care provision in Ireland and in the Netherlands is that the latter is primarily supported through private health insurance with central government paying some fifteen percent of health-care expenditures. Traditionally, health- care provision in the Netherlands has been a private sector enterprise and government has restricted its role to one of supervision and regulation. In the hospital sector, ninety percent of acute beds are in non-government controlled institutions. In 1974, the Government formulated three policy goals for the health sector; these were, equal access to health services, even distribution of health facilities over the country, and a decline in the growth of health expenditures. The growth rate fell from 10.7% in 1977, to 7% in 1982 and 4.3% in 1983. In 1985 the growth rate was 1.5%.

In 1972 the Hospital Facilities Act was passed which began the process of volume control in the hospitals. A licence was required from the Ministry of Health to build or extend a facility which required an investment of more than 500,000 Dutch Guilders. In 1979, the Amended Hospital Facilities Act required Provincial Government to draw up regional hospital plans, and on this basis licences could be granted for constructing or reconstructing hospital facilities. The regulation of specialisms within hospitals was controlled through the Sickness Funds Insurance Act which allowed the Funds to refuse contracts for new specialisms. The 1982 Health Services Act, which replaced the Amended Hospital Facilities Act, allowed regulation of the volume and quality of services. Since 1983, central government introduced regulations that required short-term acute hospitals to operate under a fixed budget system; the budgets were set at each institution's expenditure level of two years prior, adjusted for subsequent inflation. Hospitals which borrow funds on the capital markets used to have a State guarantee for these borrowings but this was ended in 1987. The situation may be contrasted with Health Board bank overdrafts which reached £36.84 million in 1986. Technically, Section 33 of the 1970 Health Act could have been used to restrict these borrowings; it was, however, only rigorously applied in 1987 with Health Boards and hospitals restricted to fixed "cash limits".

De Roo, in a review of Dutch health-care policy, has noted: "In the 1960's and 1970's the primary political justification for bringing the health-care system under central governmental control was to make health-care services of high quality equally available to every citizen of the welfare state. However, as a result of the economic distress of the 1970's, cost containment gradually superseded the earlier policy goals. As a consequence, the new laws on charges and on health facility planning more and more become instruments for cost containment. The declining growth rate has had its price in terms of increased social tensions. Hospitals complain more and more publicly about the shrinking amount of money available to them, and they try to mobilize public opinion to resist future budget cuts by arguing that they will hurt the quality of patient care. Within hospitals this leads to more and longer waiting lists for elective surgery, but also for consultation. The professional groups show growing resistance against measures designed to lower their incomes".[17]

The Netherlands provides a striking contrast, in terms of its system of control, to the Irish experience. Yet, unlike Ireland, the Netherlands has primarily a private sector or, more accurately, a corporatist, health-care sector in its organisation and finance. The impetus for State regulation resides in the Dutch tradition since the 1960's of increasing State involvement in social services provision and income maintenance supports which are generally classified as 'Welfare State'. Dutt and Costa, in a review of public planning in the Netherlands, describe the rationale for State involvement as follows: "Where care changes from being a favour to a right guaranteed by government, it is natural that government should take the initiative in planning and harmonisation... in the first place, the initiative for planning legislation developed partly in order to meet the wish for the right to co-determination expressed by the democratising movements.... Thus, there is opposition to planning legislation from private organisations and allied politicians"[18]. The degree of regulation can also impede what professionals and consumers might regard as welcome initiatives in medical care treatment. Thus, for example, the regulatory cycle for new technology or treatment provision can take up to two years or more to complete and, hence, restrict the diffusion and application of new technology.

The Netherlands has sought to constrain health expenditures

and the behaviour of the providers (hospitals and doctors) through an extensive system of legislation and regulation. This has proved successful in dampening down expenditure growth while there is evidence that consumer groups have effectively by-passed restrictions on technological application. Discretion in decision-making is very tightly constrained at a time of general unease over the growth in health service administrative costs. The 'trade-off' made in terms of control as against consumer choice (the sickness funds are private insurance funds) is not a final one. New legislation may well see a retreat from the current regulatory system to one where more choice is exercised by individuals. While there has been disquiet expressed in the Netherlands over the administrative costs of the system of regulation, this is in the context of State control of the activities of private health insurance funds. This contrasts with the same disquiet expressed in Ireland over the cost of administration in the context of public provision of health services.

The provision of the health services, funded through government expenditure or by way of private or third-party insurance schemes, is characterised by highly professional and organised personnel who are involved in the delivery of health care. Klein observes that "Welfare State services are not only manpower intensive, they also tend to be highly unionised. Consequently, we have strong representational groups, not only for doctors, nurses and teachers in the social services, but also for the less skilled or unskilled workers in them. The Welfare State thus in a sense creates the constituency for its own perpetuation"[19]. It is the case that while Ireland did not adopt the service priorities of the Welfare State (universality of service provision and access to services), the form of employment and organisation of the providers does parallel that described by Klein. In some important respects, it was incorporated in the legislation itself. Thus, for example, the powers given to Comhairle na nOspideal without, until 1984, control of financial allocation, allowed the medical profession to fashion a hospital system which was not a unitary one or subject to central control in respect of the co-ordination of public and voluntary sectors. The Minister for Health, in 1976, stated during the course of a parliamentary discussion that: "it must be known by every Deputy in the House now, that, as far as consultancy appointments are concerned, Comhairle na nOspideal - apart from the money factor - are the be-all and end-all of such an appointment"[20].

ALTERNATIVE MISSION: JOB CREATION

In 1971, the Health Boards assumed responsibility for the health services formally discharged by the County Councils (by the Health Authorities in Cork, Dublin, Waterford and Limerick).   In the early years of the Health Boards, there were numerous parliamentary questions tabled in the Dail by politicians interested in their budgetary allocations and in what was seen as the increase in administrative costs of the services. In one such question, the Minister for Health stated, in November 1971, that: "I am aware that there has been a considerable increase in hospital costs in recent years and that this is largely in line with the trend in other sectors of the economy. The increases in hospital costs can be mainly attributed to the increased cost of medicines and drugs, improved pay and conditions for staff and to general improvements and extensions of hospital services.   As the remainder of the reply is in the form of a tabular statement, I propose with your permission, a Cheann Comhairle, to circulate it with the Official Report"[21].

Estimated Costs of Health Board and Voluntary Hospitals

	1969-70	1970-71	1971-72
(a) Salaries and wages	26,584,700	33,359,500	39,843,500
(b) Food and provisions	4,029,800	4,506,600	5,054,800
(c) Drugs and appliances	3,448,600	4,177,700	4,884,000
(d) Buildings	1,778,600	1,986,900	2,323,300
(e) Others	6,746,700	7,727,300	8,963,100

"The Deputy will be disappointed to hear that the cost of the administration of the health services is only 3 percent of the total cost and I would defend that as an extremely low percentage. The cost of the new management structure of the health services has meant an increase of only a quarter of one percent of the total cost of the health services. If the Deputy wants to ask me what the likely cost is of the support staff under the Health Boards and if I subtract the previous cost of the same kind of staff working for the health authorities, the Deputy will again be disappointed to hear that the actual percentage of the total cost of the health services is extremely low"[22].

The term 'management cost' was defined as that required to install the top management structure (Chief Executive Officers, Programme Managers) recommended by McKinsey & Company. There was, of course, additional employment generated at clerical and administrative level in the health services and in 1976 the numbers were disclosed in a parliamentary question. The data disclosed a thirty-five percent increase between April 1972 and April 1976 in this staff category from 1,664 to 2,299. The relative increases in this category during the periods 1976-1980 and 1980-1984 were sixty-six percent and eleven percent respectively. The relative increases in this category during the periods 1976-1980 and 1980-1984 were sixty-six percent and eleven percent respectively. The growth of personnel in the Health Boards for the period 1971 to 1981 is shown in Table 4.2. Comparative data for growth in personnel in the voluntary hospitals is shown in Table 4.3.

On the setting up of the Health Board system, a new grading structure for clerical and administrative staff was introduced; a seven-grade structure replaced the existing three-grade system that had pertained in the old local authority structure. McKinsey had recognised that weaknesses did obtain: "Judging by the number of personnel now working on health matters in the health authorities and counties, we estimate that a total staff of over 1,000 will be required who will all have to be fitted into an equitable overall personnel structure. Moreover, in the present grading structure, several weaknesses are apparent that affect those personnel now working on health matters. Therefore, a comprehensive study of these staffing requirements should be carried out"[23].

In December 1970, a working party, representative of the Department of Health, Local Government, the Chief Executive Officers and the Irish Local Government Officials Union (now the local Government and Public Services Union) was set up to evaluate and recommend on a new grading structure. In its report, the Working Party noted that: "We were conscious of the extent to which a good, progressive grading structure could influence and improve the position regarding recruitment"[24]. The structure was installed in 1975. It gave Health Board staff a pay link with Civil Service grades, more remunerative than those obtaining in the Local Authority sector at that time, and provided a career progression hitherto unobtainable in that sector. Of some thirty-eight thousand staff in the Health Board structure, some 28,000 are "officers" of the Boards. This staff category cannot be dismissed or made redundant with a change in the relevant legislation. The Department of Health did not enjoy, until the imposition of the "public sector recruitment embargo" in 1981, close control of members and grades in the Health Boards as this was a delegated function of the Chief Executive Officer under Section 14 of the 1970 Health Act. Thus, while arbitration and conciliation machinery could control the pay within a staff grade, the central authority did not enjoy (until 1981) similar control over the numbers within a grade. Indeed, up to quite recently the Departments of Health and Finance could not agree on a figure for total numbers employed in the health services. See Table 4.4[25].

At the same time, there was a reduction in the Local Authority contribution to the health services; in 1972/3, local rates accounted for forty percent of the cost of health services, and by 1976 this had fallen to one point eight percent. To public and local political perception, therefore, health services and health service employment did not impose any financial commitment at local level. The hundreds of parliamentary questions tabled in Dail Eireann during these years on local hospital services usually requested additional facilities for hospitals in the questioners constituency.

The government election manifesto in 1977 included a commitment to the retention of the County Hospital system. It appeared that hospital services were to be retained and resourced well above a level envisaged by the Fitzgerald Report. The new government also had a specific public sector job creation programme with a target of 10,000 additional jobs, including a target of 2,900 jobs in the health services. The government, indeed, exceeded its job creation target for the health sector. In a parliamentary question on 1 February 1978, the Minister for Health gave the following information: "The total number of jobs created in 1977 was made up as follows: Non-Capital Services, 3,200, Capital Projects and maintenance works, 1,000. With the permission of the Ceann Comhairle, I propose to circulate a Statement with the Official Report showing the breakdown of the jobs between the various personnel categories. Following is the statement"[26].

Non-Capital Services

Category	No. of Jobs
Medical	210
Dental	33
Public Health Nurses, General Nurses and Allied	955
Psychiatric Nurses, Mental Handicap Nurses and Allied	442
Para-medical (including Social Workers, Occupational Therapists, Speech Therapists, Physiotherapists, Radiographers, Technicians)	389
Catering and Housekeeping	241
Administrative	36
Clerical, Typing, Receptionists, Telephonists	432
Portering	79
Ambulance and Transport	16
Child-care Staff	137
Home Help	134
Others	96
TOTAL	3,200

Capital Projects and Maintenance Works

Category	No. of Jobs
Professional	50
Craftsmen	450
Unskilled workers	500
TOTAL	1,000

An additional estimate for the Department, introduced on 8 December 1977, detailed the additional cost of recruitment in calendar year 1977 as £8,850,000. The projected trend of the increase in health service employment was given in a parliamentary question on 2 February 1978 as follows:

Date:	28 Feb 1977	July 1977	Jan 1978	Jan 1979
Department of Health	340	340	341	341
Health Boards and other Health Agencies	50,987	51,912	53,282	55,497

"Information is not available as to the extent of indirect employment".

The official Department of Health census of employment on 29 February 1980 shows the total numbers employed by Health Boards and voluntary hospitals as 55,647[28].

The increase in health service numbers coincided with significant special increases in pay for health service personnel. The cost of these increases in June 1980 was £88,390,000. In December 1980, a second supplementary estimate was introduced which provided for additional pay costs in 1980 of £17,961,000. The supplementary estimate also provided for £16,000,000 'required to maintain essential services in 1980'. The Minister for Health, in June 1982, informed the Dail that "pay costs have increased from £197 million in 1977 to about £652 million in the current year; this is due to increases in the numbers employed in the health services, the application of national pay awards to health services staff and, in particular, costly special increases for many grades of health service personnel under the established negotiating machinery". The Minister also informed the Dail that "during the course of the past twelve months because of the present difficult economic situation, the Government have found it necessary to restrain the creation of additional employment in the health services"[29].

The health service is, of course, a labour intensive service. The measurement system is there to measure the effect of personnel on the quality and quantum of care delivered; the concentration of the Irish system of measurement on input rather than health-status output is discussed in the next chapter. The 'stop-go' nature of government policy on service-provision in hospitals in 1974, 1975, 1978 and 1981 had its effect also on the administrative and management system. One senior Hospital Administrator described it thus: "the attitude in the health service was that patient need reigned supreme. Now the pendulum has swung completely the other way; the attitude now is 'how much does it cost'?"[30] A senior Clinical Consultant described the process as: "Administration do not want to measure quality; their code-word is 'adequate'"[31].

Many of the personnel interviewed in the course of this research were highly critical of the attitude of personnel from the Department of Health during the 'cutback' phase in 1987 and 1988. The Department had "opted out" of policy advice and no guidelines, save adherence to cash limits, were proferred to Health Board or hospital personnel.

The model used in this study assumes that the centre is pursuing consistent policy objectives. This was clearly not the case in Ireland. Legislation was silent on criteria for service provision (as distinct from eligibility for access to services). Administration was obliged to implement unclear policy objectives; on the one hand, hospital rationalisation, on the other hand, specific job creation targets. The next chapter describes the administrative process and it argues that in the absence of a clearly-defined strategy for the hospital sector, surrogate expressions of efficiency substituted for practical attempts to measure effectiveness.

ALTERNATIVE MISSION STATEMENTS

The discussion paper 'Health - The Wider Dimensions', issued by the Department of Health in December 1986, is the first official review of Irish health policy since 1966. The paper is, therefore, important as an expression of the civil service's view of the progress made in health care-policy over the last twenty years. The status of the document is consultative and it has not been issued as a Green or White Paper by the Government. The paper does not envisage any legislative change to clarify the aims and objective of health-care policy in respect of 'eligible' persons. It does seek, however, an enhanced role for the Department in terms of its policy-making influence in the central administrative system of government departments (Section 4.8), and that this would be reflected in legislative change. The document ranges over a number of policy issues and its framework is the World Health Organisation's 'Health for All by the Year 2000' programme which is discussed later in this chapter.

On hospital planning the document identifies the key issues

as: the continuing validity of the basis on which overall bed complements are agreed; the appropriateness now of certain services being provided on an in-patient basis; the relationships between the management of hospitals not administered by Health Boards and the providers of resources; the adequacy of the management structures of hospitals; and the precise definition of the role of individual hospitals, the range of services they are expected to provide and the population they are designed to serve[32].

On the assumption that a strengthened primary care sector can be developed, 'it is possible to deflect some of the current workload from acute hospitals'[33]. It notes that organisational innovations such as day-wards and five-day wards can improve hospital efficiency but acknowledges that their development requires "further impetus". It adverts to the need for clear co-ordination between the voluntary hospitals and the Health Board hospitals and that the Department of Health, in the past, had "acquiesced" in permitting voluntary hospitals to "see themselves as independent providers of services"[34]. On the structure of the acute hospital system it states (in a fashion very close to one of this study's propositions) that "it will be necessary in respect of each hospital to determine its role, its range of services, the population it is expected to serve and its relationship with other hospitals and community services"[35].

On the management and planning of the health care system, the document outlines "a number of problems (which) have been identified in the existing structure", including "the considerable autonomy enjoyed by Health Boards in regard to spending with little responsibility for raising revenue; the poor integration of services provided by statutory and non-statutory agencies, leading to duplication and inefficiency; and due to the programme structure, little incentive within Health Board areas for integrated planning of services across care programmes, based on measured health needs"[36].

It states that proposals have been made to Government in respect of "a formal responsibility for health promotion for the

Department of Health at national level and the Health Boards at local level; a more representative membership of Health Boards, including representation of the non-statutory sector, on each Board; a contractual relationship between Boards and non-statutory agencies providing services on their behalf; a management system in the Health Boards based on personal accountability and a more explicit reporting relationship between the Boards and the Minister for Health; a change to geographical area rather than care programmes as the unit of management; the establishment of Community Health Committees to provide a formal input for the local community to local decision-making about health matters"[37].

The document acknowledges that the changes envisaged will "pose role conflicts for many professionals who will have to become much more involved in the planning and management of services, accepting the responsibility as well as the additional influence which that will entail"[38]. The stance of the professionals to management is discussed in Chapter Six. In this regard it should be noted that their response is to see doctors in direct management positions with all other hospital staff reporting to them. It is unlikely that this is what the Department of Health envisages.

On allocation of resources, the document states that 'allocating resources on a geographic basis owes more to history than to any scientific methodology'. It proposes a shift to a system which links allocation with 'health needs in particular catchment areas', and it considers that, with no prospect of increased funding, reallocation can be made from the hospital sector to the community care area. In respect of hospital's allocation, the document states: "It is not unreasonable that hospitals providing particular services be expected to do so at a standard cost. This would require knowledge of each hospital's case mix and the costs associated with each type of case. Work on the development of such a system (based on Diagnostic Related Groups), is currently underway and it is anticipated that, when fully developed, this system will provide a basis for efficient resource allocation, initially, between hospitals. In the short term, as part of the re-organisation proposals put to government, it is proposed to change the direct funding relationship between the Department of Health and voluntary agencies and to allow Health Boards the latitude to 'shop around' in choosing suppliers of services which they do not provide direct"[39]. 'Health - The Wider Dimensions' clearly demonstrates the shift in departmental thinking from one of administrative decentralisation of the Health Boards towards one of greater central control. It proposes the re-assertion of the authority of the centre. In terms of the model used in this research it constitutes a change in the 'rules of the game'. The argument is one which stresses efficiency considerations at a time of constrained expenditures. Hallas, in a study of the efficiency and effectiveness debate in the NHS, observed: "linking efficiency with urgency is a mistake from a perspective that considered acceptability as a necessary criterion... (the) consequence... that necessarily follows from a drive towards effectiveness and efficiency is a greatly increased use of overt and covert rationing"[40].

Chapters Five and Six describes the existing measurement and management characteristics of the health-care delivery system and it will be seen that it is, in large measure, not consistent with the proposals of the Department of Health. Indeed, in some respects it may not be the view of government, as the Minister for Health in 1988 asserted that he was satisfied with the existing administrative arrangement of the Health Boards.

The Irish Medical Organisation responded to the discussion document and their general conclusions were as follows: "there are enormous presumptions made that there will be, as a result of the policies proposed, a major change in the attitude and responsibility of the public towards their health. No evidence is presented to support this claim. It will not be possible to change the emphasis in the health services as radically as proposed without additional resources being allocated at least for the initial period to allow the new structures in primary health care to become fully operational.... It is further assumed that any shift from hospital/institutional care to community-based care will of itself provide better and possibly more cost-effective care. There is considerable doubt about both assumptions"[41]. The 'vision' preferred by the Department is one of rationality, systems and procedures. The experiment in administrative regionalisation of service delivery is now to be replaced by more central control in Dublin. One Chief Executive Officer's view was that "we are looking for U.S. standards at Third-World prices"[42]. It would, indeed, appear that the centre could not hold.

The administrative centre of the civil service did not enjoy much control or sense of purpose during the latter end of the 1970's, and the McKinsey model of 'staff-line' management was never pursued, especially in the direction of the development of performance indicators. Legislation was deficient in this area and no incentive was available (due to continued increase in resource levels) to develop systems of control and performance measurement. The Department of Health did 'pilot' a number of schemes in areas such as Diagnostic Related Groupings and computer-based accounting packages in certain Health Boards and hospitals; these are detailed in the following chapters. There was not, however, an overall health-care policy but rather a concentration on the provision of health-care resources - more hospitals, new jobs and diagnostic equipment. When resources were constrained in the early 1980's, the overdraft facilities of the Health Boards cushioned the blow and until 1987 the 'crisis' did not emerge fully-blown onto centre stage. The alternative mission statement of the World Health Organisation's 'Health for All', which emphasised primary-based care, was seized upon as a way out of the dilemma of hospital-care politics. To a large degree, however, the adoption of the WHO strategy was a selective one and it is evident that there was much in this programme which would not easily be fitted into the pragmatic, functionalist and political world of Irish health-care policy. This is not to suggest that the adoption of a preventive community-based, health-care policy is a tactical stratagem on the part of the Department of Health. Rather that such a policy, to be effective, has to take into account the existing weakness in legislation and the rigidity of the resource allocation system. It is also the case that such a policy requires performance measurement which takes account of the inherent uncertainty of medical practice, and a management system that can cope with a fundamental re-orientation of strategy. It is argued in Chapter Five that the Swedish measurement and information system in health care provides a clear example of how legislative aims, management control and political impetus combine to give coherence to health-care strategy formulation and implementation. In the Irish case, the measurement system is not capable of such support, nor is the incentive structure geared to the proposed re-orientation of health-care policy.

WORLD HEALTH ORGANISATION AND SWEDISH HEALTH-CARE LEGISLATION

The WHO strategy for health-care in the year 2000 is primarily concerned with the socio-economic determinants of health status and the reorientation of health service policy towards a preventive, community-based, approach. The policy entitled 'Health for All by the Year 2000' was agreed in 1984. The first target states: "by the year 2000, the actual differences in health status between countries and between groups within countries should be reduced by at least 25%, by improving the level of health of disadvantaged nations and groups"[43]. In its suggested solution to this problem, the WHO states: "the target on health inequalities present a challenge; to change the trend by improving the health opportunities of disadvantaged nations and groups so as to enable them to catch up with their more privileged counterparts. Within individual countries, this implies above all a need for willingness in recognising the problem, for initiative in actively seeking information on the real extent of the phenomenon, and for political will in designing social policies that go to the root of social group formation, in terms of guaranteed minimum income, assurance of the right to work, active outreach services to assist the groups in need, etc."[44].

It is clear that if Ireland was to seek to achieve these targets, which are primarily rooted in social, economic and resource considerations, then legislation would need to be altered, not only in organisational terms, but in ways which mirrored the equity considerations outlined in the target above. It is the case, however, that the WHO programme, which is the intellectual basis of 'Health - The Wider Dimensions', is not congruent with the stated position of civil servants or politicians when changes in Irish health-care policy provision are mooted.

Thus, for example, the research programme adopted by WHO includes a priority to be given to research on inequities in health. The WHO document states: "the two basic goals of health-care are to raise the overall level of health and to increase equity; inequities may relate to social status or class, sex and gender, ethnic grouping or geographic location. Three types of research are needed with regard to equity; theoretical and methodological work on concepts and indicators of health inequalities; a better understanding of the factors and mechanisms that create and maintain health inequalities and policy research and evaluation of programmes aimed at reducing health inequalities"[45]. To monitor progress, it is suggested that countries must carry out routine data collection that bears on health differences; the Irish statistical base is discussed in the next chapter and it is clear that such data collection is not done on any systematic basis. It contrasts with the Dutch and Swedish response to the challenge posed by economic constraints in health service provision. This disparity also extends to the measurement system used in these countries where there is a clear concern to review the practical effects of health-care policy.

The Swedish health-care system is a decentralised one with the twenty-three County Councils having responsibility for health-care provision and expenditure, which are primarily based on local taxation (see Table 4.5). The Swedish policy on health services, which is oriented to the implementation of the WHO 'Health for All' programme, began with a series of research programmes in 1978. These were published in 1982, and circulated to politicians, health-care professionals and the public. The Act of Parliament, which was based on these research proposals and documents, was passed in June 1985. The guidelines underlying the Act HS-90 were: "(a) health care must be characterised by active health policies; (b) the need of the population for care must determine the allocation of health-care resources; (c) health-care resources must be weighed against socio-economic and employment goals and limitations"[46]. The discussion document focussed on issues such as socio-economic differences in health-care utilisation, social and occupational distribution of prevalent diseases, and correlation between health hazards and illness groups.

The legislation states that health-care on equal terms requires: (a) "equality in the supply of resources available throughout different parts of the country; (b) equality in the utilisation of care between different groups of society; (c) equality in terms of access to care; (d) equality in terms of quality and efficiency of care"[47]. The administrative system used to implement the legislation is described in Chapter Five. It is important to note here, however, that the Swedish system does provide a clear example of congruence between strategy, measurement and management. The social and political consensus in Sweden, relative to the aims and objectives of health- care policy, is in marked contrast to the Irish data discussed in this study.

NATIONAL ECONOMIC AND SOCIAL COUNCIL (NESC)

The NESC, in a wide-ranging study entitled 'A Strategy for Development 1986-1990', considered future options for health-care policy, based on their previous reports which dealt specifically with health-care, and the work of A.D. Tussing on an economic appraisal of general practice in Ireland. They recommended that: "firstly, the pattern of demand, as distinct from its quantity, should be redirected towards the more cost-effective sectors of the health-care system. This, in turn, implies that changes in the incentives and remuneration system, consistent with the analysis above, should be implemented. Secondly, the supply of the most expensive resources, namely hospital beds, should be controlled.... Ireland's hospital bed provision is higher than that of the U.K. or of Denmark - another small, somewhat rural society"[48].

On private health-care insurance (which is discussed in Chapter Six), the NESC stated: "a further specific issue arising from the general analysis of health service utilisation, but with an added redistributive dimension, is the question of tax subsidised private health care. 'Private' health care, in the Irish health-care regime, is often significantly subsidised by the public health system - this cross-subsidisation arises from the use which consultant hospital doctors in public hospitals may make of publicly-provided amenities for their private patients who do not bear the economic cost of their utilisation. Tax allowances need to be considered in the light of this subsidisation. In the light of the fiscal constraints, the efficiency implications of induced demand for health care, and the equity aspects of both health care and taxation, the Council therefore recommend curtailment of this tax allowance"[49]. On employment levels in the health-care sector, the NESC noted that: "almost two-thirds of current health expenditure consists of 'pay' items; aggregate real pay has declined by 7% from 1980 to 1985; and health services manpower numbers have fallen somewhat since 1981 (the number of GMS doctors has been rising however). It will be clear that wider policies regarding manpower levels in the public service and public sector pay level will have a crucial effect on health services expenditure"[50].

Tussing, in a review of the decision-making process in 1987 and 1988 on health-care budgets and policy, observed that: "patients and, even more so, providers have felt that the depth and speed of the cuts were punitive in their impact. In this connection, it should be noted that to the extent that the speed and depth of cuts remedy errors made in the past, the errors where those of the centre, i.e. the government, the Department of Finance, and the Department of Health, and not those now being asked to pay the price"[51].

The inference is that the system is the creation of the central policy makers in Dublin and of the politicians. This is the case in certain important respect but it is to ignore the role of Health Boards and doctors in the process. It is the case that legislatively there are no indicators of quality or span of service provision nor, indeed, is there in the administrative sphere, apart from the 'norms' of bed numbers and recommendations of Comhairle na nOspideal on minimum consultant staffing requirements. The eligibility criteria, based primarily on income, for access to free services is not systematically monitored; for example, there are no publicly-available data on waiting lists and there are acknowledged deficiencies in service provision in dental, aural and opthalmic services between the Health Boards. The NESC policy observations (they are based primarily on non-hospital data) do not extend to any discussion of the mission of health care insofar as it relates to the social or economic determinants of health needs. The Government, in its overall macro-economic strategy since 1987, have based their stance on the NESC document. While not accepting the recommendation on abolition of tax-exemptions for private health insurance, they have accepted the general observation on the need for a reduction in bed numbers. The implementation of this policy (the new 'norm' is now to be 3.7 acute beds per 1000 population) has, perforce, been the provenance of the Health Boards for public beds. The data in 1988 suggests that the Boards are cutting acute beds in the large general hospitals as well as in the smaller district and general hospitals. The Department of Health do not have the capacity to 'target' specific hospitals or hospital beds in the public sector as this is a legal function reserved for the Boards.

Within the existing administrative structure, the voluntary

hospital sector is the one more open to direct influence from the centre. This is achieved via the 'budget'; the Department can allocate monies which are insufficient to cover the year's running costs and, hence, the independent voluntary Board of Management have no other option except closure. The closure of smaller voluntary hospitals, which are then relocated to new modern sites, is designed to modernise hospital-based medicine in Dublin and Cork. In the public sector, however, the Department does not possess such direct influence. They are reliant on Health Boards which have political and geographical constituencies and are subject to pressures of local service demands. The President of the Irish Medical Organisation has observed this process to be one where the Department "has abdicated its responsibility in this area and attempted to leave the decision-making to the elected Health Board members, the vast majority of whom do not have the knowledge or expertise to make the necessary decisions"[52].

CONCLUSION

The criticism levelled at the Department of Health for 'opting out' of the policy process in respect of the 1987 and 1988 expenditure allocations was a direct result of the absence of a mission in the Irish health-care system. It is, in one important respect, an unfair criticism; that is, the legislative base for health-care is a function of government and not the civil service. An important lesson to be gained from the comparative data is that government must attend to the basic policy process of formulating a mission for a national system of health-care. Legislation would then provide an effective framework for the control of the service delivery system and it would assist in the management of the professionals within it. Without such a mission statement, publicly-funded Irish health care will continue to be subject to the exigencies of political fortune and its control will be vested in the unstable relationship between the centre and the producers of the service.

The data presented in this chapter give rise to the following central conclusions. The regionalisation of health service delivery did not address the basic issue of health-care policy in Ireland; no clearly-defined legislative statement (or administrative mechanism) exists to define the quality or range of services for 'eligible persons' - in itself the only approximate strategy statement in Irish health-care legislation. The lack of specificity in legislation can give rise to a capriciousness in decision-making in the administrative 'centre' which owes more to impotence of a civil service which lacks consistent government policy than it does to the rational claims of technocratic management. The reform programmes on offer - unlike the Swedish and Netherlands experience - do not address the need for balance between all parts of the system - legislative, administrative and professional.

If you do not possess a clearly-defined legislative strategy for a national health-care system, how then do you measure progress or monitor the effectiveness of expenditure? The following chapters describe the experience of Ireland, Sweden and the Netherlands in this area and it will be seen that the Irish health-care system became primarily a producer-oriented one with little 'voice' for the consumer or taxpayer.

FOOTNOTES

1. Quoted in Department of Health, **Circular Letter** 155/30, Meitheamh, 1972.

2. D. O'Mahony, "How Should the Plan be Interpreted", pp.31-32 in **Irish Banks Review,** Dec. 1984.

3. **Health Act,** (No. 28 of 1947), 1947.

4. B. Hensey, **The Health Services of Ireland,** 1969, p.26 and pp.21-22.

5. **Health Act,** (No. 26 of 1953), Section 14(2).

6. R. Barrington, **Health, Medicine and Politics in Ireland 1900-1970,** 1987, p.248.

7. **Health Act, 1970,** Section 45.

8. **Dail Debates,** Vol. 239, Column 1633.

9. Quoted in **Irish Law Report Monthly,** 1986, McMeal vs Minister for Health, p.622.

10. Ibid, p.618.

11. **Health Act, 1970,** Section Six.

12. Personal Communication, 11 Nov., 1987.

13. Section 72 of the 1970 Act states:
    (1) The Minister may make regulations applicable to all Health Boards or to one or more than one Health Board regarding the manner in which and the extent to which the Board or Boards shall make available

services under this Act and generally in relation to the administration of those services.

(2) Regulations under this section may provide for any service under this Act being made available only to a particular class of persons who have eligibility for that service[15].

14. R.F. Bridgman and M.I. Roemer, **Hospital Legislation and Hospital Systems,** 1973, p.153.

15. Myles Tierney, **The Parish Pump,** 1982, p.71.

16. Personnal Communication, 11 November 1987.

17. A. de Roo, **Health Care in the Netherlands** (Mimeo), Erasmus University, 1987.

18. A.K. Dutt and F.J. Costa, **Public Planning in the Netherlands,** 1985, pp.90-91.

19. R. Klein, "Values, Power and Policies", p.171, in OECD, **The Welfare State in Crisis,** 1981.

20. **Dail Debates,** Vol. 299, 1976, Column 1229.

21. Ibid, Vol. 257, 1971, Column 689.

22. Op. cit., Column 690.

23. Department of Health, **Towards Better Health Care,** Vol. 1, p.3-3, 1970.

24. Report of Working Party, "Evaluation of Executive and Clerical Jobs in Health Boards and Local Authorities", Dublin, August 1971 (unpublished), p.32.

25. **Department of Finance,** 1987.

26. **Dail Debates,** Vol. 335, June 1982, Columns 1031-1032.

27. Op. cit., Columns 591-592.

28. Department of Health, **Statistical Information Relevant to the Health Services,** 1981, p.63.

29. **Dail Debates,** Vol. 335, June 1982, Columns 1031-1032.

30. Personal communication, 26 August, 1987.

31. Personal communication, 24 June 1987.

32. Department of Health, **Health - The Wider Dimensions, 1986,** p.64.

33. Ibid, p.65.

34. Ibid, p.65.

35. Ibid, p.66.

36. Ibid, pp.70 and 71.

37. Ibid, pp.70 and 71.

38. Ibid, p.72.

39. Ibid, p.82.

40. J. Hallas, "Acceptability in an Effectiveness and Efficiency Climate", p.91 in A. Long and S. Harrison (ed) **Health Services Performance,** 1985.

41. Irish Medical Organisation, **Response to Health - The Wider Dimensions,** 1987, p.16.

42. **Personal communication,** 10 November 1987.

43. World Health Organisation, **Targets for Health for All,** 1985, p.24.

44. Ibid, p.26.

45. World Health Organisation, **Research for Health for All: Vol. 1, Research Policy, 1987,** pp.11-12.

46. National Board for Health and Welfare, **HS-90 The Swedish Health Services in the 1990s,** p.3.

47. Ibid, p.51.

48. NESC, **A Strategy for Development 1986-1990,** No. 83, 1986, p.215.

49. Ibid, p.216.

50. Ibid, p.216.

51. A.D. Tussing, "The Recent Cuts in Irish Health Expenditures", p.343 in **The Irish Medical Journal,** Vol. 80, No. 12, Dec. 1987.

52. K. Egan, "The Health Cuts and the Irish Medical Organisation", p.345, in **Irish Medical Journal,** op.cit.

CHAPTER FIVE

Measurement of Health Care Expenditure

In any discussion of national or international trends in health care expenditure, and the management of the hospital system, attention has to be paid to the time at which certain initiatives were taken and the economic conditions which obtained at that time. Chapter Two has described the underlying administrative and political assumptions that led to the creation in 1970 of the regional form of health administration in Ireland. The data in this chapter show that the Irish experience of increased health-care expenditure is part of a world-wide phenomenon with the exception that, in Ireland, the increased "lagged" behind that of our European neighbours. It will be shown, however, that the Irish response to expenditure restraint was different from that of other European countries. Lacking any clear strategic objectives, the Irish system of control consequently lacked any relevant information on which to base expenditure restraint. The administrative centre did not have appropriate 'means of influence' to fashion a new medical, administrative or financial structure that would accommodate the health-care system with the financial reality of the 1980's.

A central issue in control is the relationship between the allocation system (the budget) and the measurement process. Here, the budget is conceptualised as the agreement between the financiers of the service (State, taxpayer) and the providers of the service (hospitals and the professionals). If it is the case that the budget process is not effective - for example, if large deficits are allowed - then it is likely that the interested parties will not give priority to the measurement system as there will be no incentive for installing effective control. The notion of 'slack' - resources over and above those required to discharge the functions of the system - is relevant in such an environment. The function of management is to install a control system to ensure that the aims and objectives ("the mission") of the hospital sector are being met on the basis of financial, social or legislative criteria ("rules of the game") agreed between the financiers and providers of the service.

This chapter forms part of the test of two of the research propositions: because of the lack of an objective statement of mission, the general hospital sector has no defined role and no rational system of resource allocation, and as a result the control system has developed no objective or measurable norms. The propositions are designed to show that, in the absence of a clearly defined health-care strategy, measurement will concentrate on the activities or inputs of health-care personnel rather than on the outputs of their activity. It has already been shown that the medical care environment is a highly uncertain one and government policy in Ireland exacerbated this uncertainty through its job creation programme. Concentration on resources has engendered in the health service a producer-oriented perspective that is, itself, highly dependent on economic growth or government borrowing. The Department of Health's discussion document - "Health - The Wider Dimensions" - issued in 1986, is used here as the most recent official statement on health service management. The document acknowledges that there is a need for a re-definition of the role of the acute hospital sector, a revised basis for the allocation of resources to the hospitals and a redistribution from this segment to the primary and community care areas. One can use these prospective policy statements to examine the current status of the measurement system and to assess the feasibility of altering it without recourse to legislative change in the "rules of the game". That is, how effective can measurement and control be in a system that has, as Ireland, ill-defined aims and objectives?

MEASUREMENT OF HEALTH-CARE RESOURCES

The comparison of national trends in health-care inputs can cast more shade than light. Different national accounting standards, variations in medical practice and the lack of

HOSPITAL REGION OF SWEDEN

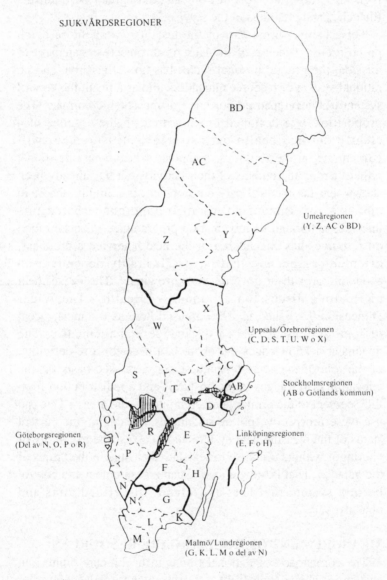

SJUKVÅRDSREGIONER

BD

AC

Umeåregionen
(Y, Z, AC o BD)

Z   Y

X

W   Uppsala/Örebroregionen
(C, D, S, T, U, W o X)

C

S   U   Stockholmsregionen
T   AB   (AB o Gotlands kommun)
D

O

Göteborgsregionen   R   E   Linköpingsregionen
(Del av N, O, P o R)   (E, F o H)
P

F   H

N

N   G

L   K

M   Malmö/Lundregionen
(G, K, L, M o del av N)

.... länsgränser

disaggregation in health-care budgets combine to make comparative analysis difficult, if not, at times, improbable. However, as an OECD (1985) study remarks: "by and large the long-term trends for individual countries are likely to be more accurate than the comparison of level differences between analogous items; the most reliable form of international comparison is likely to be that between national rates of growth in the main areas under examination. All appear to have experienced a very rapid expansion of health services up to around the mid-1970's, followed subsequently by a deceleration"[1].

Table 5.1 sets out the 1982 per capita expenditure on medical care for the OECD countries, and Table 5.2 total health expenditure expressed as a percentage of gross domestic product (GDP). Ireland, in common with France, Japan, the Netherlands, Norway, Sweden, Spain and the United States have experienced a doubling of their health to total expenditure ratio. Table 5.3 shows the ratio of total health expenditures of GDP, as well as the ratio of public to total expenditure for Ireland, Sweden, the Netherlands, the United Kingdom and the United States.

There are no satisfactory indicators of health sufficiently disaggregated and sensitive which can relate changes in health status to specific changes in health service provision. Thus, traditional indicators of crude mortality ratios are still utilised in most national and international studies, together with life expectancy, morbidity rates and/or levels of functional disability in individuals. One report observed: "by some estimates 80 percent of all deaths and an even greater percentage of total disability are now due to chronic illness. Little is known about the causes of these chronic diseases. It is unlikely that medical breakthroughs will cure chronic diseases, since much of it is simply due to the natural ageing process and deterioration in the functioning capacity of body organs"[2]. The absence of linkage between health expenditures and health outputs is, of course, a serious technical problem when one wishes to assess the relative impact of a change in health-service provision. The evidence that "life-style" illnesses (tobacco, alcohol, diet and road-traffic related injuries) are a major contributor to health status has been the impetus behind the 'preventive' approach in the medical-care model. Thus, an individual must take responsibility for his actions and life-style and, hence, reduce self-inflicted illness. Such an orientation can be reinforced through various methods of co-payment or indemnity insurance so that a person will 'share' the cost of his treatment with the State or insurance company. However, this approach runs up against arguments of equity (in terms of the influence of socio-economic status on health outcomes) and administrative simplicity (cost of administering 'selective' versus 'universal' benefit schemes).

"Health - The Wider Dimension" states that there is, in Ireland, as elsewhere, a lack of linkage between resources devoted to health-care and improvement in health status: "it is a matter of concern that despite the increasing level of resources devoted to health services over the past two decades, the level of health in the population did not show any marked improvement"[3]. Comparative data for Ireland, Sweden, the Netherlands, the United Kingdom and the United States shows that the respective increases in terms of the absolute total and average annual gains in additional years of life occured in the 1900-1950 period[4].

The lack of linkage between an increase in hospitalisation rates and mortality/morbidity ratios has resulted in two distinct policy initiatives. The first, is the re-orientation of health-care away from the medical-centred emphasis on "cure" in an institutional setting to a community-based preventive approach. The economic environment of most European countries, with deficits on current account and low growth rates, adds further impetus to this re-orientation. The case to support the contention that community-based medicine is more economical is unproven and, indeed, what evidence there is suggests the contrary[5]. The second policy initiative relates to the evidence that hospitals, increasingly driven by high-technololgy innovations, are substantially increasing the source intensity per patient treated. The DRG system in the United States is one example of pressure exerted by financial agencies to curb this phenomenon. Another, albeit organisational response, is that of the Health Maintenance Organisations (HMOS), pioneered in the United States which are also seen as alternatives to the traditional divide between primary care and the hospital systems. The DRG system is discussed below and the HMO model is outlined in Chapter Six.

RESOURCE ALLOCATION AND HOSPITAL BUDGETS

Table 5.5 summarises the hospital reimbursement system in several OECD countries. In the light of the many and varied methods for payment, the OECD concluded: "annual budgets have the advantage of simplicity and overall expenditure control, but do not necessarily provide strong incentives for micro-efficiency or quality. Per-diem payments also have the advantage of simplicity and fewer disincentives than global budgets for quantity and quality perspectives, but since per-diem payment systems provide incentives for increased length of stay per admission, they do not (in the absence of volume controls) provide incentives for limiting overall expenditures. Thus, it would be expected, a priori, that prospective total budget approaches inclusive of in-patient physician services such as the British National Health Service would result in lower expenditures than would a retrospective per-diem cost or charge-based system with physicians being paid on a fee-for service basis"[6]. The lack of fit between prospective payments, based on a standard-cost model such as the Diagnostic Related Groupings, and a 'closed' system of funding, based on 'earmarked' central government allocation, in the Irish context, is discussed below. A link between the desire for financial and technical efficiency and control of social expenditures is, of course, the behaviour of the key personnel in the delivery of service - the health professionals. Chapter Six examines this linkage and it argues that, in the Irish context, it is one of the important decisions that has to be taken if a balance is to be struck between social cohesion and professional autonomy, as existing incentive structures for the professionals are not in accord with a policy of resourcing non-hospital care.

The Irish system of control is deficient in terms of the budget process and, indeed, the process itself departs from the original legislative intent as set out in the Health Act, 1970. While administrative convenience has vitiated legislative intent, it is the case that the current method of hospital budgeting has involved the Department of Health in decision-making which runs directly counter to the intended 'staff' role envisaged in the PSORG model (see Chapter Two). The Swedish data demonstrate that it is not sufficient to alter the budget system to achieve strategic health-care policy objectives. Thus, while there are proposals to alter the system for Irish hospital budgets, no legislative change is contemplated. Given the data in this study, it is unlikely that such a functionalist approach will be successful.

Within the hospital segment of the health-care system, there are two main activities being performed. The 'care' activities which relate to the non-medical aspects of the hospital and which include such matters as "hotel" or accommodation facilities. The 'cure'activities - the medical professionals - are by far the most significant in terms of cost and the delivery of medical services to patients. The intrinsic uncertainty of medical practice, the lack of linkage between inputs and outputs and the interdependencies of each level in the system of care has generated a substantial interest in the appraisal of hospital-centred care. A WHO study has described the problem as follows: "most hospitals are now facing the most severe difficulties they have encountered for decades, and that for many the question is not how they can expand their roles, but rather how they can survive their present financial crisis. Added to this are the problems of management; insufficient numbers of appropriately trained managers at every level of the health system, including hospitals"[7].

Table 5.5 sets out the average number of cases treated per hospital bed per year in respect of Ireland, the Netherlands, Sweden, the United States and the United Kingdom. In the Irish case the data shows an increase in bed utilisation which is consistent with the financial data and the expenditure on hospital consultant appointments which is discussed later in this chapter.

The model used for hospital budgetting in Ireland is an incremental one; that is, last year's outrun is utilised as the basis for the current year's allocation. In no case, recorded by the author, did hospital administrators or managers see any linkage between the activity rates of their hospitals and their annual budgets. Since the budget is based on bed-occupancy, consultant staffing and the specialisms within a hospital, accurate information on the actual costs of the hospital's operations are essential. In large measure, up to 1989 such information was unavailable. Some hospitals, notably the public voluntary hospitals, developed in-house, computer-based accounting packages that facilitated department-based budget control. The development of management information systems by the Department of Health is an endeavour shrouded in controversy. The Department opted for an imposed strategy of standardisation of computer hardware and packaged software which, in the words of an internal civil service working paper, became "the main controversy in public service computing". A single contract was awarded to McAuto - a subsidiary of the McDonnel Douglas Corporation - to computerise the health sector. In a submission in 1986 to the Dail Committee on Public Expenditure, the Department reported that the cost of the computerisation programme since 1981/82 was some £10 million and that full computerisation of the entire health sector was estimated to be in the region of £40 million. The internal working paper concluded its review of the computerisation programme as follows: "there is evidence that some Health Boards and hospital administrations are not lending their support to the policy. Progress to date, with the full implementation of the system in the pilot sites, has been slow. Only parts of the total system are in place. On the whole, the wisdom of a centrally imposed, relatively inflexible, solution is seriously questioned by the problems to date in the health sector"[8].

The programme of computerisation did not, however, assist greatly in the basic accounting or audit function upon which the budget allocation system is dependent. In 1987, the Department of Health had to order a special audit for 1986 (the 1984/85 audit was not completed) to allow it to implement the proposed cutbacks in expenditure. The 1987 allocation included a sum of £12.6 million to pay off "arrears on balances" incurred by the Health Boards and voluntary hospitals in their overspending on authorised allocations in previous years. A Department of Health official remarked that the Department's "biggest failure has been in the area of measurable norms"[9].

REVIEWS OF HOSPITAL PERFORMANCE

In a study of the effectiveness of the acute hospital sector, Blaney observes that "the ultimate objective of the hospital system... would be to contribute substantially on a value for money basis to the health of the community... in the absence of experimentation, it is impossible to separate the role of the hospital from the contribution to health of other sectors of the health service...."[10].

Since 1974 the Department of Health have commissioned a number of internal studies dealing with many aspects of the hospital system; these studies include reviews of hospital admission rates, appointment of consultants, use of pathology services, five-day wards, and projection of demand for maternity beds in Dublin. A striking feature of these studies is the underdevelopment of the basic information data-base in the hospital sector which is consistent with the proposition that the control system has developed no measurable or objective norms. Another feature of these reports is the call for the development of national policy guidelines in, for example, admission policies and pathology services.

A study on the costs of consultant appointments stated: "it is difficult to identify and quantify the full additional expenditure implications of appointments in very large hospitals. In County Hospitals it is a more manageable exercise as fewer appointments are made and changes in workload/expenditure can more readily be associated with particular appointments"[11]. Table 5.6 sets out the comparative costs in 1981 of a selected number of hospital consultant appointments. The 1982 study further noted that "the level of... information is quite inadequate at present (and) the first step to cost control is to discover where and why costs are being incurred and steps can then be taken to adopt control measures where appropriate"[12].

In 1986, the Department of Health undertook a pilot exercise in four hospitals in the area of Diagnostic Related Groupings (DRG) which is a "classification of the patient population into classes with similar expected output utilisation (and) allows for the resources consumed and costs incurred to be related to the types of patients or case-mix that the hospital treats". The DRG method is utilised in the United States as a prospective payment system for hospital reimbursement for Medicare patients. The method can, as Luft observes, be seen as "either competitive or regulatory". In the Irish situation it would appear that the Department considers that the method is a regulatory one and can be used to fund hospital budgets. Such a change, which is highly dependent on information technology requirements, would involve a significant shift in the current organisational and budget system in Irish hospitals. It would also be a second-order decision, as firstly the role and functions of each hospital within the system would have to be defined and agreed. The need for definition of the role of hospitals is acknowledged; 'Health- The Wider Dimensions' states: "it will be necessary in respect of each hospital to determine its role, its range of services, the population it is expected to serve and its relationship with other hospitals and community services"[13]. A recurring theme of this study is that the existing organisational arrangements for health-care planning and management are not based on objective or measurable criteria and that the overall system lacks coherence in policy aims and objectives. While the Department of Health's own statements mirror (in some cases quite closely) the research propositions, the 'lack of fit' between policy statements and operational reality is quite large. Thus, for example, in spite of the lack of policy on service norms in respect of the programmes for health service delivery, the 1988 allocation letters to the Health Boards stated that they: "should ensure that key services for the old and housebound be protected, services such as Community Nursing services, Home-Help Services, and Meals-on-Wheels, services for the Handicapped, Child Services, particularly daycare and pre-school services for deprived and disadvantaged communities and aftercare services for children leaving long-term residential care, are maintained at 1986 approved levels in real terms"[14]. The policy directive was "translated" by one Health Board as follows: "it is clearly not possible to carry out these requests within the level of funding provided. It is necessary, therefore, to again examine each individual service and to determine if it can be delivered in a manner or at a level which will be more cost-effective or efficient without causing deprivation or hardship".[15]

The reasons for the 'lack of fit' were the neglect of the measurement process, the divide of the hospital allocation function(split between the Department for public voluntary hospitals and the Health Boards for the public hospitals), and the separation of consultant appointments from the resource allocation function. The latter is described in the next chapter. Over and above these features, is the lack of a clearly-defined mission: the Swedish experience, discussed later in this chapter, shows a clear congruence between legislative intent and the measurement process.

RESOURCE ALLOCATION AND ADMINISTRATIVE REVIEW

It is clear from the discussion in Chapter Four that the Irish legislation in 1970 did not provide a mission or strategy statement for health-care policy. It is also the case that the 'staff-line' management structure (involving the devolution of responsibility for service delivery) was crucially dependent on the development of performance indicators. Professor Borgenhammer, in a study of budgetting in the Swedish health-care system, describes the process as follows: "two methods based on different principles are available for the financing of health services. One is the method of the free market, where supply and demand are balanced by means of prices. The other is grounded on the allocation of tax revenues according to a formal political decision process.... In public administration contexts priority-setting and resource allocation generally emerge as a process of political negotiation"[16]. A senior Irish Department of Finance official characterised the process to the author as: "the Department of Health was the 'post-box' for the Health Boards. They did not develop criteria for the allocation of resources for the Health Boards"[17]. The assessment of the financial function in the Health Boards was described in a 1975 review as requiring "the development of measures of effectiveness. Success in doing this was seen as dependent on incentives to the people who would be operating the services"[18]. A senior official of the Irish Department of Health, in describing the budgetting process in the voluntary hospital sector in 1987 (which has 50 percent of acute bed numbers), observed: "lay administrators are at a disadvantage in facing up to the clinicians. We cannot match up to the professional expertise of the consultants"[19]. The administrative arrangements, and the underlying management model for the Irish Health Board structure was described in Chapter Two. In 1970, McKinsey & Company, the management consultants, described the process of setting performance indicators as follows: "building a programme structure on objectives and accounting for expenditure will not be sufficient to answer the key question on how to allocate resources. The structure will not tell you how effective the services are, what is the level of need in the community, on how to plan to meet the need. To answer these questions, the Department must identify, and agree with the Boards, a common set of indicators for the whole service"[20]. In 1987, one Chief Executive Officer of a Health Board observed: "when services were expanding in the 1970's, it was a case that the Health Boards had to persuade the Department that developments were necessary, as no policy was 'coming down' from the Custom House"[21].

PROGRAMME BUDGETS

In the Irish context, the major objective in setting up the Health Boards in 1970 was the political-administrative desire to see Irish health-care upgraded to European standards of the time. A Department of Finance official characterised the Health Boards as "unashamedly expansionist", and a senior Department of Health official remarked that "the system identified, promoted and rewarded people who were good at developing services"[22].

The approach taken to the budgetting and control of Health Board activities was to group similar activities into "programme areas" and McKinsey & Company recommended three such programmes, Community Care, Special Hospital Care and General Hospital care, and stated that "a programme consists of a coherent group of services available for patient care"[23]. The formal structure of the Government Appropriations Accounts (sums granted for public services) did not, however, change significantly to reflect this programme structure (see Figure 5.1). The Department of Finance did, in 1984, issue statements of Comprehensive Public Expenditure Programmes which set out expenditures under each programme area.

In respect of consultant-staff hospitals (i.e. Regional, County and Public Voluntary Hospitals), the objective of the programme is stated as: "to ensure that persons who require acute hospital care are provided with such care at the appropriate level as quickly as is required, and that they are effectively and efficiently treated"[24]. It is the case, however, that the structure of accounting or 'vote' system for the health service in general does not allow (even if resources permitted) for a redistribution between programme areas. The Department of Finance view each programme area (and associated 'sub-vote') as "walled-off" from each other and, hence, no "trade-off" between programmes is sanctioned. Thus, at the heart of the allocation process there is a rigidity which makes it difficult to implement a policy of a strengthened primary care sector. A graphic illustration of this budgetary intertia is shown in Figure 5.2 which sets out for the Western Health Board the allocation of each £1 in grant-in-aid for the years 1971 and 1987[25].

Reference has already been made to the budget process as an agreement between the financiers and the providers of a service. Table 5.7 sets out the Supplementary Estimates for the Department of Health during the period 1973-1980. It will be seen that, unlike our European counterparts, Irish health expenditures continued to show significant increases after 1975. A major component of the supplementary monies were pay and grading awards to health-care staff which are examined in Chapter Six. Over and above the grant of supplementaries was the ethos that was engendered in the Health Boards and hospitals as a result. One former Chief Executive Officer put it thus: "in the first few years... a certain latitude in expenditure and control was justified, but after that it should have been imposed from Dublin. There was no development of standards or norms for measuring effectiveness and the pressure to spend more was coming from Dublin. Thus, our Health Board was contemplating a four percent increase in services while the Government was pressing for a six percent increase"[26].

The Controller and Auditor General, in 1975, stated in respect of the accounting controls in Health Boards that there were "inadequate standards of accounting and recording" for the years 1971-1973 and in the case of one Health Board that "the documentation... was less than that demanded to conform with the requirements of public accountability"[27].

The basic element of a control system is, of course, the accounting procedure for budgetary allocations. In 1971 the Secretary of the Department of Health wrote to the Chief

Executive Officers of the Health Boards as follows. "it is recognised that the development of the management accounting function which is key in the proper implementation of Programme Budgetting will present some difficulty. While a number of possible solutions have been considered, it is the Department's view that the Health Boards will have to rely on the resourcefulness and adaptability of the Finance Officers in developing this function, while, at the same time, making arrangements to train and develop the persons below the Finance Officer who will have direct responsibility for management accounting"[28]. The Department itself issued revised sets of accounts and procedures for the Health Boards in February 1976, January 1978, and November 1979. Yet, in 1987, a senior finance official in the Department of Health stated that "the Health Boards never produced a proper balance sheet, merely an abstract of accounts"[29].

The lack of fit between the programme budget model, the Department of Finance allocation (or vote) process, and the system of Health Board accounting had an impact at the political level. In the course of debate in 1976, an Opposition spokesman stated, in respect of the proposed health vote allocation, that: "So far as I am concerned, it is all very dubious. Were the budgets, as originally submitted, not genuine? Were they not prepared on a prudent, economic basis? Were the Executives in the Health Boards guilty of irresponsible, careless budgetting and financing? If the team of officials from the Department of Health could come along and revise the budgets so that the deficits disappeared, surely something was wrong in the first instance?"[30]. The failure to control health expenditures affected relationships at the administrative centre, between the Department of Health and the Department of Finance. One health service administrator describes it as follows: "between 1982-86, the Department of Health, in view of the shifts in Government policy, did not have a clear view of the evolution of the hospital system, and, to that extent, they did not exercise control. The Department of Finance did not know the internal workings of the hospital system sufficiently well to exercise control and they did not have a good relationship with the Department of Health"[31]. An Assistant Secretary in the Department of Health, describing the process of managing in a period of austerity, stated: "since 1981, we have gone through a number of identifiable phases. We have had an initial period of denial and delay; then we have taken once-off measures which did not require major changes in the system and brought about some savings; now we have accepted that the change is long-term and that our structures, systems and people must be geared to manage for results and quality care...."[32].

The absence of specific objectives, together with a measurement system that did not develop performance indicators, meant that decisions had to be taken on the allocation of priorities in a less-than-rational manner. A Department of Finance official put it thus: "the Government itself have very badly articulated priorities for social expenditures and the choice of programmes where restraint or cutbacks are proposed can operate on the "suck-it-and-see maxim"[33].

THE IRISH SYSTEM OF MEASUREMENT: COMPARATIVE ANALYSIS

Measurement systems and management control cannot be separated from the mission or objective of the enterprise. Chapter Four discussed the experience of Ireland, the Netherlands and Sweden in health-care legislation and in the social framework that influences national strategies in health-care provision. A related feature of measurement is the degree to which the persons whose activity or performance is being appraised are integrated with the social, ethical and financial objectives of the organisation. Chapter Three has discussed the regulation of professions and the next chapter looks at the practical expression of this regulation as seen by the remuneration and incentives offered to the health-care professionals in the European countries studied in the research. What is important in the control of health-care expenditures is not simply the normative prescriptions of legislation, the public-private mix or the financing structure, but rather that there should balance between all of these features. That is, the mission statement should be clearly stated and understood and the measurement-motivation system must be in accord with what is a social and political decision.

Chapter Four has discussed how the legislative control of the hospital segment, by way of the Regional Hospital Boards, was vitiated by administrative and political neglect.   That is, the concept of regionalisation for hospital services (the primary objective and recommendation of the 1968 Fitzgerald Report) was never followed through in practical financial management. To some extent, this failure owes more to the 'lack of fit' between a technocratic formulation of management process and the political reality of County Council geographical imperative than to any inherent defect in the original recommendation. The practical effect, however, was to separate the budgetting and control of Regional Hospitals (whose catchment areas overlap Health Board administrative boundaires) from the day-to-day service imperatives of their high-technology, capital-intensive functions.   Each Regional Hospital located within a Health Board region was deemed to be self-sufficient in financial terms, ignoring the transfer of resources (by way of treating patients from another region) between regions.   The case of the Dublin voluntary teaching hospitals is different, however, in that the Department of Health apportions a 'notional' share of their resources from the allocations of the Health Board regions outside of Dublin. The 'transfer' is not a popular one and has led to the notion of regional 'self-sufficiency' in medical specialisms.

In Sweden, acute hospital services, other than County Hospitals, are divided into six regions (see map).   While the County Councils are administratively and financially responsible for medical services, the financing of the Regional Hospitals is a shared function discharged by a Regional Board. The following section describes the process as it operates in the Gottenburg

Region[34].

Sweden is divided, for Regional Hospital services, into six regions and the Western Board consists of four counties and the Gottenburg County Borough (city). The Board, which, in law only has consultative status, is concerned with the allocation of the budget to the tertiary medical activities of the two regional hospitals situated in Gottenburg and, on this definition, Gottenburg City does not refer any patients outside of its hospitals. The region's population is approximately 1.5 million. The budget operates on the payment system that the four counties "buy" their tertiary care from Gottenburg's tertiary hospitals. Each month, the counties pay one-twelfth of a notional estimated yearly budget, based on their previous year's payments. This is then balanced to reflect the actual costs in March of the following year. Gottenburg region has a computerised 'patient specific' accounting system which in its cost-estimation technique is similar to the DRG system. However, the notion of a 'fixed' DRG cost-reimbursement is not considered suitable to the Swedish system as they consider tertiary care to be a regional matter and, therefore, if a DRG was to operate, Gottenburg County would be penalised as 'costs' would be attributed solely to them. A schedule for the apportioning of indirect costs have been agreed at Board level; for example, in surgery an average of 50 percent and in medical cases some 20-30 percent of total costs is attributed to tertiary care. While Gottenburg are the primary buyers of capital equipment, the regional element of these costs are recouped through a depreciation factor built into their 'charges' to the counties. While the Regional Board only has consultative status, in practice their recommendations are accepted by the counties. In large measure this is achieved by having the 'political heavyweights' in the counties directly represented on the Board. No medical personnel sit on the Board, but their representatives are consulted at the administrative level. The Board operates with the technical expertise of the counties and it has a total staff of seven. While the State controls entry into medical schools and subsequent specialities, it is the counties' responsibility to decide on the number and grading of its medical personnel. Thus, for example, there is a current national shortage of radiologists and nephrologists which results in 'overbidding' by the County Hospitals for such staff. That is, the less well endowed counties will tend to create more senior (and costly) positions to attract specialists than the more favoured location such as Gottenburg City. In the 1960's, Sweden was generous in its financial allocation to medical services. The economic environment of the 1970's was less favourable and politicians now take a much tougher stand on resource allocation questions. Productivity, as a result of standstill or reduced resources, has increased at the Regional Hospital in real terms in the last few years. It will take another 3-5 years before the County Hospitals show a similar trend. The County Councils operate and control some 95-97% of all medical services in their areas. Private interests have mainly concentrated on out-patient services in urban areas. More recently, there has been the development of private medical clinics where high-technology operations such as coronary bypass can be bought. However, the 'private' customer must first be referred by the county medical system and, in this way, the expense falls on the county for private medical care.

The audit of county health expenditures (reliant as they are mainly on local taxation) is subject to the audit section of each County Council. This process has been developed in recent years and the Confederation of Swedish County Councils has re-oriented the audit process away from cost accounting to activity or process audit.

A central and striking feature of Swedish health system is the organisation of research and analysis into the practical effects of health care provision. Chapter Four has already discussed the research and analysis which preceded the change in Swedish health care legislation that resulted in the Act HS-90. Both Sweden and Holland, which have very different financial structures for health care provision, have long 'lead-times' between the declaration of intent for administrative/financial change and the actual bringing in of the legislation. The main organisation whose task it is to undertake this research is the Swedish Planning and Rationalisation Institute for the Health and Social Services (SPRI). Established in 1968, SPRI is jointly funded by Central Government and the County Councils, with the latter paying two-thirds of the annual budget of SEK 57 million (1984). Its main functions are to: i) support, co-ordinate and participate in planning and rationalisation of medical care; ii) collect and distribute information within the health-care sector; iii) establish Swedish standards for hospital equipment and consumables; iv) facilitate co-ordination between health and medical care, and the social services[35].

The activities of SPRI have ranged from assessment of medical technology, comparative studies of the impact of differences in medical practice, cost effectiveness studies of medical care provision and, more recently, the development of quality assurance programmes. These studies, which are published and which contain explicit data on both medical and financial variations among County Council's hospitals are utilised in the practical mangement of health care provision. That is, politicians are keen to have reason for wide variation in the cost of 'their' hospital or health service.

Thus, for example, the conference organised to study cost-effectiveness in health-care, was attended by local County Councillors whose task is to manage the health-care budgets in their counties. The link between planning, measurement and mission is stated by one local politician who addressed the conference: "an unfortunate element exists today in discussions concerning medical care and other social services within the public sector. The argument is that planning is unnecessary now when the social economy is unbalanced. My opinion is definitely the opposite. Planning is much more needed during harsh times, not for continuing expansion, but for less expansion and for reallocation. Development, research and commitment from the health care professionals is also needed. This is to prevent crash landings or to meet the problem as a guest in reality"[36].

SPRI have organised Consensus Conferences, designed to document the present medical, technical and economic evidence on common medical procedures or ailments. The intent of these conferences, attended by politicans, administrators, physicians and the press, is that agreement will be reached on the topic and, hence, a common approach will be used in decision-making in the County Councils, hospitals and health-care centres. Consensus Conferences have taken place to date on Sight Improving Surgery, Diagnostic Imaging of Liver Tumor, Treatment of Depressive Disorders, Urinary Incontinence in Adults, Treatment of Myocardial Infarction, and Total Hip Replacement.

The contrasting approach of the Irish, Swedish and Dutch governments to financial planning in time of restrained expenditures can also be seen in the public nature of the latter two countries'policy statements. In a 1986 document, the Netherlands' Minister of Welfare, Health and Cultural Affairs published its financial projections for health care for the period 1986-1990 (see Table 5.8). While the Swedish plan HS-90 (given the decentralised management and financing systems) does not contain disaggregated projections on expenditure, it does contain quantitative estimates of the cost and manpower requirements required to meet HFA 2000 targets. Thus, for example, doctors (which in 1983 represented 4.9 percent of health service personnel) are expected to increase to 6.0 in 2000 together with an increase in nursing personnel from 21 percent 1983 to 24 percent. A pertinent assumption in the plan is that staff costs will approximately follow the rate of economic growth (Chapter Six reviews the Irish experience in this regard). 'Health - The Wider Dimensions' (which is not yet accepted as official government policy and issued as a White Paper) does not contain any qualified estimates of projected expenditures, nor does it see a need for any strategic shift in the role of government in health-care delivery. It states that "no good reason has emerged for changing the dominant role adopted by the State in relation to health-care in Ireland"[37]. This contention is, of course, non-operational in the sense that it does not say what, if any, changes are proposed in the practical arrangements for the management of health-care delivery. While the document does refer to issues such as public-private mix in hospital provision, it does not specify how the task of co-ordination might be improved.

CONCLUSION

The objective of measurement is to assess the performance of the system relative to agreed objectives or policy. In the absence of agreement on objectives, measurement can become a routine process and the control system itself can become a surrogate for policy. In large measure, the Irish system of control in publicly-funded health-care became just that - a cost accounting mechanism for health-care expenditures, rather than the assessment of performance based on agreed policy objectives. In addition, the very purpose of information was itself misconstrued - the administrative centre viewed it as a focus of control and not as a measure of performance that could be used to assess the adequacy of service delivery. The only available 'norms' were those of bed norms and the informal consultant staffing norms of Comhairle na nOspideal - and as Klein remarked in respect of bed norms in the NHS in the United Kingdom "in practice these turned out to be somewhat metaphysical concept, as it became clear that the relationship between means and aims was highly problematic and uncertain"[38].

The many devices for expenditure restraint (cost containment is, in reality, a misnomer) such as DRG's, Health Maintenance Organisations and Peer Review (a quality control function) are related to national, organisational, cultural and budgetary issues and, hence, do not easily 'transport' to different countries. It is clear, however, that Irish health-care expenditures have not been the object of any sustained scrutiny and that such appraisals that have taken place are not embedded in any systematic model. The lack of a mission statement hinders measurement as no impetus is available other than the exigencies of budgetary restraint. The next chapter examines the relationship between the control system and the professional and administrative staff within the health services. It will be argued that the 'rules of the game' in large part excluded this sector from the measurement system and, hence, the notion of control became instead a 'vocabulary of exhortation'.

FOOTNOTES

1. OECD, **Measuring Health Care 1960-1983,** p.10.

2. OECD, **Financing and Delivering Health Care,** 1987, P.35.

3. Department of Health, **Health - The Wider Dimensions,** 1986, p.54.

4. See **OECD,** 1987, op.cit.

5. See for example, WHO, **Economic Research into health service growth,** EURO Reports and Studies No. 52; Pekurinen, Vohlonen and Hakkinen "Reallocation of Resources in Favour of Primary Care: The Case of Finland", WHO Working Paper 1987.

6. OECD, op.cit, pp.26-27.

7. World Health Organisation, **Hospitals and Health for All,** 1987, pp.69-70.

8. Department of Finance, Internal Working Paper, 1987.

9. Personal Communication, 22 July 1987.

10. R. Blaney, "Applications of Evaluation in Acute Hospital Care", p.103 in W. Holland (ed) **Evaluation of Health Care,** 1983.

11. Department of Finance, **Appointment of Hospital Consultants** (unpublished) 1982.

12. Ibid, paragraph 6.4.

13. **Health - The Wider Demensions,** op.cit, p.66.

14. Department of Health, **Allocation for Non-Capital Expenditure, 1988,** paragraph 9(11), Circular Letter, 27 Deireadh Fomhair, 1987.

15. North-Western Health Board, **Allocation for Non-Capital Expenditure, 1988,** paragraph 6.3.

16. E. Borgenhammar, **Health Care Budgetting,** 1979, p.5.

17. Personal communication, 30 June 1987.

18. Department of Health, **A Review of Irish Health Services,** 1975. Part III.

19. Personal communication, 18 December, 1987.

20. Department of Health, **Towards Better Health Care, Vol.1,** 1970, p.1-6.

21. Personal communication, 11 November 1987.22.

22. Personal communication, 22 July 1987.

23. **Towards Better Health Care,** op.cit.

24. Department of Finance, **Comprehensive Public Expenditure Programmes, 1984,** p.251.

25. **Western Health Board,** Annual Budget Report, 1987, p.22.

26. Personal communication, June 1987.

27. **Appropriation Accounts, 1975,** p.xxxviii.

28. **Circular Letter P44/50,** 29 October 1971.

29. Personal communication, 20 July 1987.

30. **Dail Debates,** Vol. 289, March 1976, Column 274.

31. Personal communication, 14 May 1987.

32. "Whither The Acute Hospital System", p.14, Address by Mr. J. O'Dwyer to National Conference on the Health Services, Dublin, October 1987.

33. Personal communication, 30 June 1987.

34. The description is derived from a meeting with Dr. Jan Speek, Regional Hospital Board (Planeringsnainnden), Goteburg Region, Oct. 20, 1987.

35. SPRI, 1987-1989, **Spri Tryek** No. 154.

36. SPRI, **Cost Effectiveness in Health Care,** Spri Tryek 091, 1985, p.4.

37. **Health - The Wider Demensions,** op.cit., p.33.

38. R. Klein, **The Politics of the National Health Service,** 1983, p.78.

CHAPTER SIX

Management of National Health Care Systems

Central to an appraisal of health-care provision (or, indeed, any public service) is the role played by the providers of the service. Care has to be exercised to ensure a balance between the resources devoted to the staff and the actual volume of service provided. In health-care, as in education, where staff costs account for upwards of seventy percent of overall costs, attention has to be given to the providers of the service as well as to the 'demand' for the service. The literature on this subject ranges from the 'capture' model, where the providers 'capture' the controlling agency, to propositions of 'slack' and bargaining, where incremental decisions to coalitions in the organisation result, over time, in resources being given to personnel that are additional to those required for the discharge of the organisation's functions. In health-care economics, the work of the 'York School', which sees control of professionals as paramount, is the dominant tradition[1]. Another important viewpoint is that of the Institute of Economic Affairs (IEA) where the emphasis is placed on the deregulation of State control with the consequent re-assertion of consumer sovereignty in the health-care 'market'[2]. These two perspectives result in distinct, but not wholly separate, policy prescriptions for the management of health-care systems. The former stress organisational and structural responses, on behalf of the State, to curb the influence of the doctors which results from the asymmetry of information in the 'market'. The latter, while recognising the asymmetrical relationship, advocates the dismantling of the State's regulation system (by, for example, removing the monopoly position of State-registered medical practitioners) and increasing the purchasing position of the consumer in the market. The 'York School' approves of central funding for health-care provision while the IEA advocates a shift to private insurance with a 'minimum' floor for public provision.

Back of these perspectives is, of course, the role of the State in devising national strategies for medical care. The interplay of strategy and measurement was discussed in Chapter Five and it was shown that the linkage between them was the arrangements made for the governance and control of professional and administrative staff. These arrangements are given expression in, for example, salary and conditions of employment, the autonomy of action of professionals and the relative strengths of accountability and private control of public resources. We have already seen how weak the budget instrument is in the Irish context. It has not been effective in ensuring that the structure of the hospitals and the management of professionals within them is in line with stated government policies of redistributing resources to non-hospital care. Attention is centred here on private health insurance and its effect on the behaviour of hospital administrators and doctors in the context of the weak control system that pertains in the hospital segment of the Irish medical care delivery system.

This chapter examines three of the research propositions; because the Irish hospital system has developed no objective or measurable norms, resource allocation is highly centralised in Dublin, that professionals within hospitals have created and captured slack for their own benefit and that there is no impetus to clarify the mission of the health-care system as a whole. There is a tension between the regulation of medical personnel and their need for professional autonomy and administrative requirements for accountability in public expenditure. Chapter Four has identified another important feature of administrative control - that the political and administrative 'centre' pursue consistent policy objectives and, thus, achieve a balance between strategic objectives and day-to-day control. In the Irish case, such a balance was not struck largely due to inadequate legislation and employment creation programmes which weakened the centre's capacity for effective control.

In reviewing the evidence and data presented in this chapter, it is important to recognise that the policy decisions that were taken on, for example, the method of payment for general practitioners and for hospital consultants were the result of the interplay between the State, as financier, and the professional aims of the doctors. The final choice was not inevitable or, indeed, for that matter the most effective. Chapter Two described the important unresolved issues of management control that were not attended to in the legislation or in the administrative arrangements for regionalisation - in particular, the separation of the approval of consultant appointments from the budgetary allocation system for hospitals. In addition, these unresolved issues were tackled on a one-by-one basis and the resultant incentive structure - both for doctors and management - gave rise to serious co-ordination and control problems in the Regional Health Boards and in the acute hospitals. Thus, quite apart from the ambiguity in policy and the neglect of measurement, one had an incentive structure that influenced the behaviour of professionals and managers in ways quite different from the implicit policy objectives of the 'centre'. It is clear that, without appropriate legislation to focus the investment decision, one of the central control features of European health care systems is absent in Ireland. That, together with the diversity of incentive structures, meant that the Irish system was over-dependent on administrative compliance, and underdeveloped in its strategic base. The management of public sector agencies is problematic without clear strategic objectives and appropriate measurement systems.

COMPREHENSIVE HEALTH-CARE PLANNING

The Health Act 1970 was primarily designed to implement the re-organisation of the general practitioner service and the regionalisation of hospital services; the fusion of these two objectives resulted in the setting up of eight Regional Health Boards. The decision to have eight regions was not, however, inevitable and, indeed, it ran counter to one body of opinion within the Department of Health; the personnel involved in hospital services considered that three regions (on the basis of the Fitzgerald Committee's recommendations) were sufficient[3]. It is also the case that the primary impetus for the 1970 Act was the 1966 White Paper - 'The Health Services and Their Further Development' - and that the 1968 Fitzgerald Committee's recommendations were (in the description of one senior Department of Health offical) "stitched into" the prospective legislation[4]. This may well account for the subsequent demise of the Regional Hospital Boards which were designed to co-ordinate hospital budgetting and review of performance in the hospital sector. At the core of the legislation, therefore, one had two quite distinct objectives - re-organisation of primary care and regionalisation of hospital services. In addition, no agreement was made with the medical profession, until after the passage of the legislation, on the remuneration method that would prevail in the re-organised system.

GENERAL MEDICAL SERVICE

The negotiations on the method of payment for general practitioners (the medical side wanted a fee-per-service and the Department of Health favoured a capitation scheme) lasted from March 1967 to June 1971. The scheme (known as the General Medical Service), formally adopted in September 1971, was a fee-per-service one. It was agreed after the passage of the Health Act 1970, and was based on the assumption of an eligible patient visiting the General Practitioner 3.5 times per annum. The scheme came into operation in the Eastern Health Board on 1 April 1972, and in the remainder of the country on 1 October 1972. In a review of the scheme's operation in 1973, the average visiting rate was 5.5 visits per patient, about double the figures suggested by the medical organisations during the course of negotiations and the appropriate fee level. The British Medical Association used the terms of the scheme in their negotiations with Department of Health in Britain: "the item of service system of payment in the Irish Republic has made conditions of practice better there than in Great Britain and hence the significant contribution of Irish graduates to N.H.S. general practice has been diminishing"[5]. Indeed, the Department of Health, in October 1974, held that, on the basis of its operation to date it was open to them to propose a reduction in the fee from 80 pence to 61 pence[6]. In November 1974, it was recommended that fee should attract the general increases under the National Wage Agreements. A subsequent arbitration in February 1975 resulted in a further 10 percent retrospective increase, and since then fees and allowances have been adjusted in accordance with appropriate provisions of national agreements. In 1979, an arbitration agreement awarded an increase of 12.5% in fees and allowances[7].

Tussing, in a study of the general practitioner service in 1980 (whom he described as the 'gate-keepers' to the health delivery system) found evidence of "self-interested demand generated by some Irish G.P.'s"[8]. He concluded that, as the incentive structure favoured increased utilisation (for Category 1 patients), the scheme should be extended to all of the population while "charges for out-patient hospital and consultant specialist services and for in-patient hospital care, for those who currently receive these services without charges" be imposed[9]. He concluded that the net expenditure effect would be neutral.

The perspective of the present argument is the 'open-ended' nature of the GMS commitment as a charge on Health Board budgets. Thus, Health Board management have no control of their primary care budget insofar as it relates to the GMS service. Indeed, the Health Boards have on numerous occasions requested that they should have more control of the scheme. The 1984 Report on the general medical service observed that "it is in relation to cost containment that greatest concern has been expressed by management. The financial structure of the service is open-ended particularly in regard to the generated costs of drugs and the cost of referral to hospital.... Given a fee structure the annual cost of the scheme is determined by the visiting rate and associated prescribing costs. Thus, the Department may estimate, with a greater or lesser degree of accuracy, the annual costs arising from the operation of the service but, in practice, policies to control costs are limited to the monitoring of claims...."[10]. While the Working Party recommended more local involvement in the administration of the scheme, it did not advert to the need for a change in the basic budget management system; that is, Health Boards were not to have control of an important area of their expenditure and it would continue to be administered at national level.

The contract for general practitioners was revised in 1988 and the main change has been the shift in the method of remuneration for Category One patients from an adjusted fee-per-item to a capitation fee. In this manner the Department of Health will have a greater control over the total expenditure in the scheme, as estimates of projected expenditure will be more easily calculated. It should be borne in mind, however, that the new contract may well significantly change the incentive structure for individual G.Ps. Thus, where heretofore there was an incentive to see Category One patients as often as possible, now the incentive may be to refer them on to outpatient clinics in hospitals. It is too early to verify if this will happen, but it is evident that the new contract's incentive structure runs counter to the policy of increasing emphasis on primary care.

CONSULTANT MANPOWER AND REMUNERATION

The approval of consultant appointments in the acute hospital sector is a function delegated to Comhairle na nOspideal, set up under Section 41 of the 1970 Health Act. The Comhairle was, from the outset, restricted in its decision making since the original proposals of the Fitzgerald Committee (Chapter Two) were not formally accepted as government policy and it had, therefore, no politically accepted model for the acute hospital sector. A further constraint on the Comhairle, largely a result of the lack of a national plan, was described by a former Chairman: "at any time in the 1970's, the room for positive action by the Comhairle resided in the developing areas of medical practice rather than in the longer established disciplines that were embedded in the existing organisational and institutional framework"[11]. The lack of a national plan and the inertia of the existing institutional framework, affected the decisions of An Comhairle. In its second report, Comhairle stated that it had to sanction appointments (a doubling of consultant staffing in medicine, surgery and anaesthesia in Nenagh, Portlaoise, Tullamore, Mullingar, Cavan and Mallow hospitals) which "some members considered might not be in the best interests of hospital medicine in this country in the long term. The situation has been a source of concern to members and has sometimes forced the Comhairle to appear importunate or impatient when statements of policy are, no doubt for good reasons, not forthcoming"[12]. In the periods 1972-75, 1975-78, 1979-82 and 1982-85, Comhairle approved annual percentage increases in consultant manpower of 4%, 5%, 3% and 1%. In its fourth report for the period 1982-1985, Comhairle stated: "distribution of available resources, particularly medical staffing, leaves much to be desired in terms of equity. The existing financial system... does not appear to be capable of facilitating the transfer of resources to areas of relatively greater priority based on objective measure of medical need"[13]. Table 6.1 sets out the consultant manpower in each Health Board region for 1987.

The Department of Health recognised the difficulty presented by the approval of medical consultant manpower being separated from the budgetary function. In 1982, it requested that all applications for consultant staffing, whether additional or replacement, be first routed through the Department for an assessment of their financial implications. By May 1987, some seventy-five posts had been approved by Comhairle for which funding was unavailable (see Table 6.2). At the time the Department changed the approval process, Comhairle had approved some six hundred and ninety-four medical consultant appointments[14].

The Comhairle did not succeed in gaining acceptance for a single selection procedure for hospital consultants in Health Board and public voluntary hospitals, which it saw as important in shaping a single unified hospital system. The opposition to a common selection procedure came largely from the public voluntary hospitals[15].

There was, therefore, a real problem in the control of hospital consultant appointments; for some ten years approval for a post was administratively separate from the allocation of consequent resources to the hospital. Chapter Five has described the inadequate cost accounting function in respect of consultant appointments and the data in this chapter indicates that the allocation process was operating in a policy vacuum as no national hospital plan existed. The net effect was to distribute expensive manpower and equipment across a wider number of hospital centres than that considered optimum by the Fitzgerald Committee.

CONSULTANT REMUNERATION IN THE GENERAL HOSPITAL SYSTEM

Consultants in the public voluntary sector were paid on a 'pool' basis while their counterparts in the Health Board hospitals were salaried[16]. A working party was set up in December 1977 by the Minister for Health to investigate the feasibility of ensuring a closer uniformity of practice between the two sectors in areas such as terms and conditions of employment, recruitment and selection. While the medical profession had a clear objective in the negotiations - they wished to break the fixed-rate per twenty-four hours - the Department of Health entered the discussions without any clear negotiation stance[17]. This may well have been reflected in the fact that the Working Party was given no specific terms of reference and it adopted the following: "In the context of the present level of eligibility for hospital services, to examine and report to the Minister on: 1) the form of contract of employment to be entered into between consultants and their employing authorities (e.g. Health Boards and Public Voluntary Hospitals); 2) the feasibility of applying this form of contract to certain consultants who are attached to private hospitals, and 3) the establishment of a common selection procedure for consultants employed by hospitals providing services under the Health Acts[18].

The Working Party considered the issues arising from consultants treating non-eligible patients (Category III) and the consequent right of the consultant to engage in private practice. It held that

(i)   each consultant shall be entitled to have provision for private practice in his contract;

(ii) private practice outside the hospital in so far as it does not prevent the fulfilment of the terms of the contract, shall not be restricted;

(iii) medical need shall be the overall criterion for hospital services, and admissions should be governed accordingly. However, a hospital authority may, if it thinks it necessary in the interests of persons in the area it serves, limit the facilities to be made available in or at the hospital for non-urgent cases which are fee-paying patients of the consultant.[19]

In defining the duties of a consultant, the Working Party laid particular emphasis on the "unique position" of the consultant in the hospital and "that he cannot shed the continuing responsibility for his patients so long as they remain in his care"[20]. The Working Party, in paragraph 2.3 of its Report, outlined the broader responsibilities of the consultant as follows: "being a consultant also included, to such extent as may be relevant in the case of each appointment, responsibility for the running of his particular department or unit of the hospital and for the maintenance of medical standards; involvement in in-service teaching and training of medical staff, in research within the hospital, in administration outside the management of his own particular department or unit of the hospital and in those matters which the employing authority and the consultant agree are appropriate"[21].

On the important issue of measurement of a consultant's workload, the Working Party stated: "it is not proposed that there should be an exact measurement of the time spent by a consultant in discharging his contract"[22]. This clause was specifically written into the formal contract for consultants. In the case of the wider responsibilities outlined above, the contract stated: "paragraph 2.3 of the Interim Report also outlines certain other considerations which are inherent in the appointment"[23]. The net effect was to provide for no other duties save those of medical care of patients, which was itself not the subject or review or appraisal insofar as these involved non-medical matters, such as eligible or non-eligible patients, or resource-intensity per patient.

PRICING OF CONSULTANT APPOINTMENTS

An arbitrator was appointed in July 1978 to fix the remuneration of the Common Contract. While bearing in mind the medical organisation's emphasis on the unique features of a consultant's work, the Working Party considered a diverse range of salaries which included: "(a) the higher paid posts in the various departments of the Civil Service; (b) the higher paid posts in the employment of the Local Authority and Health Services; (c) the top posts in the various semi-State bodies; (d) salaries payable to top management in the private sector, as outlined in the reports published by the Irish Management Institute and Inbucon/AIC Management Consultants; remuneration of members of the Government and of the Judiciary; (f) some of the higher paid posts in the private sector and the level of earnings in some of the professions insofar as information was available, particularly from reports of the National Prices Commission"[24].

In the review of the proposed conditions of the Common Contract, the Chairman held that: "In considering the appropriateness or otherwise of the present salary levels for Health Board appointments as a guideline for determining the remuneration under the Common Contract, it must also be borne in mind that the Common Contract represents an improvement in the conditions applicable to consultants under the existing Health Board Contracts in a number of important respects. In the first place, the entitlement to engage in private practice under the "model" 27-hour contract would appear to be less restricted than the set formula which applies in the case of the present "whole-time" appointment. Secondly, it is proposed to make a special payment for the first time to cover the availability of the consultant when rostered on an 'on-call' basis, whereas this feature of his work was hitherto regarded as being compensated for by the inclusive salary at present payable. Thirdly, a new and revised method of payment for off-duty emergency work will be implemented as the '(c)' factor in the Common Contract.... Fifthly, the greater part of the cost of professional indemnity insurance will be paid by the employing authority for the first time. Sixthly, it is intended that for superannuation purposes the pay of the consultant will be reckoned as a combination of the payments he receives for the '(a)' and '(b)' factors, and the possibility remains that the payments for the '(c)'factor will also be included. These significant improvements in the current conditions of the consultant's employment with the Health Board make it all the more difficult to contend that the salaries now payable fall far short of what would be the proper remuneration for a consultant who was about to enter into a new Common Contract."[25]

In summarising the proposed new salary structure, the Chairman held that: "Indeed, it would be difficult to justify the recommendations made by strict reference to many of the salaries now paid for posts in the public sector which may fairly be regarded as involving comparable responsibilities and importance to the position of medical consultant. This means that any advance that may be secured in the public sector in the near future (over and above what may be termed 'general round increases') would not carry with it an automatic entitlement on the part of the consultants under the Common Contract to seek a further increase in the rates herein recommended, but any such application would have to be considered on its strict merit as a completely new application. Part of the justification for the increase in salary was held to be the large number of unfilled consultant appointments in the hospital sector".[26]

Chapter Six has outlined the cost implications of additional consultant appointments in the hospital sector and the lack of an admissions policy in the hospitals which would allow for an appraisal of a 'norm' for hospital admission. One feature of the Working Party's recommendations was that the scope of a consultant's job included such matters as involvement "in administration outside the management of his own particular department or unit of the hospital".This was not formally specified in the legal contract of employment. Nor was measurement of the consultant's activity. Thus, there was no incentive for the consultant to engage in cost-containment or efficiency in his use of resources nor, indeed, any formal arrangement open to administrative management to engage the consultant in joint working relationships on these matters. At the time of negotiation of the Common Contract in 1979, issues such as these were considered inappropriate or irrelevant to the Irish system as resources seemed to be available for continued expansion. As the nature of the environment changed in the 1980's, neither administration nor the professionals had the organisational structures or legal competence to engage in these issues. The lack of measurement within the hospital system has already been outlined in Chapter Five. The effect, in the "cutback period" of the 1980's, was that no mechanism was available to balance the conflicting legitimate demands of professional autonomy and social concern to ensure a uniform system of medical care delivery. The tension is usually described as a "two-tier" system of medical care, and it is discussed in Chapter Eight.

PRIVATE HEALTH-CARE INSURANCE

When the Common Contract was being negotiated, private health insurance available through a State-sponsored body - The Voluntary Health Insurance Board (VHI) was taken out by some fifteen percent of the population. Table 6.3 sets out the growth in the private insurance market. While it was not specifically adverted to in the negotiations (which were limited in their remunerative aspects to Category 1 patients), it was an assumption of the Department of Health that this figure would remain stable. It now stands at some thirty percent of the population. A review of the activities of the VHI by a Dail Committee described its function as: "the VHI is designed to perform a "residual" function, filling gaps left by less than universal eligibility and less than comprehensive coverage of the State Health Services. In general, the VHI is complementary to such services. For example, when changes in eligibility for the Health Services were introduced in April 1979, the VHI simultaneously introduced complementary changes in its own schemes"[27]. Subscribers are permitted to deduct premiums, in full against taxable income. The Commission on Health Funding estimated that the relief was in the order of some £44 million in 1989.

In a submission to the Dail Committee, the Irish Medical Union stated: "the Voluntary Health Insurance Board fulfils a vital role in the provision of payments for medical services. Since the establishment of the Voluntary Health Insurance Board in 1957, there has been a regular increase in the number of persons who are insured by the Board. As the cost of providing hospital treatment increases, the Board ensures by its schemes that medical care is available at a reasonable cost to its members. The Board plays a major role in maintaining private practice as a right of patients".[28]

The fees to consultants for services to VHI subscribers are negotiated on a yearly basis between the VHI and the medical profession. A number of the VHI described the process as follows: "the original strategy adopted by the VHI on professional fees and appropriate insurance fee units for their members was to pitch the cover on the basis of the "going rates" then charged by medical consultants. In this context, for the first fifteen years, the VHI saw themselves as a financing agency. Since then, the perception of their role altered and they operated as a co-operative or mutual trust agency and asked themselves the question "what could they do for their members". From the mid-1970's the VHI "dragged their feet" on the fee schedule payable to medical consultants. This was due to the observed phenomenon that consultant fees continued to "leapfrog" the floor price per diagnosis promulgated by VHI. They consider that they have established a norm for diagnostic fee payments in the private hospital segment. Within the private hospital segment, the VHI has relied on their growing number of members to "squeeze" inefficiencies out of the system; that is with bed numbers held constant the demand would depress the duration-of-stay periods. For example, over the last two years the total bed days for VHI patients were down three percent in each of the years. The move to the 'managed care' regime, which will yield greater information on each diagnostic procedure, should continue the efficiency drive".[29]

The VHI pay 'hotel charges' for their patients while in hospital. The escalation of hotel charges has been the most 'abnormal' cost element in VHI costs in the year 1982-1987. The VHI paid £3 million to public hospitals for hotel charges in 1982 and by 1986 this figure had risen to £26.5 million. Table 6.4 sets out the charges for the period 1980-1986. The designation by a public hospital of a "discretionary" bed (in effect a private bed) provides it with additional non-direct revenue as the cost is met by the VHI. Additionally, of course, the 'discretionary' bed also provides a source of potential revenue for the hospital consultant. On average, consultants receive £24,000 per annum from the VHI for services to their subscribers. This is in addition to the base salary of a consultant of £32,000 per annum[30]. The hospital consultant's salary is abated by twenty percent in the Eastern Health Board, by fifteen percent in Southern, South-Eastern and North-Eastern Health Boards, and by ten percent in Western, North-Western, Mid-Western and Midland Health Boards to take account of the private practice arrangements under the Common Contract.

ADMINISTRATIVE MANAGEMENT AND THE ACUTE HOSPITAL SECTOR

The Health Board structure, with political representatives in the majority on the Board and with local participation at county level and below (through the Local Advisory Committees), combined a new regional administrative management system that was, and is, without parallel in the Irish administrative system. The recommendations of McKinsey & Company were designed to implement the model of decentralised 'line' management with central policy control shared between the Boards and the Department of Health[32]. Chapter Five has reviewed the underdevelopment of the control system and the absence of performance measurement indicators in the Health Board and hospital system. The structure and efficacy of the health care delivery system was rarely a political issue in the 1970's when resources were available for service expansion. At a time of constrained resources in the 1980's, however, the political and administrative centre began to question the utility of the system. The debate has taken two main lines: growing dissatisfaction of the administrative centre with the management structure in the Health Boards, and the lack of co-ordination between it and the public voluntary hospitals, and political questioning of the value of eight Health Board regions.

In addition, Health Board managers and some individual hospital consultants are aware of the deep divide that separates the administrative and professional grades within the system. As reviewed in Chapter Four, however, the alternative strategy (or mission) statements do not address the basic issue at the heart of the debate -how is the Irish health-care system to be organised and controlled within an explicit policy framework that would align resource allocation and policy objectives? The debate has, in reality, centred on the cash limits policy of resource allocation and the apparent recalcitrance of the institutional framework to accommodate the 'new reality' of the 1980's.

McKinsey & Company recommended that Executive Committees be established in the large acute hospitals with four main areas of responsibility: to make recommendations to the Programme Manager on overall objectives and major policies (and through the Programme Manager to the CEO and Board); to manage the hospital to achieve the objectives agreed with the Programme Manager; to promote measures to improve efficiency in the hospital, and to co-ordinate activities of the medical, administrative, para-medical and nursing staffs[32]. The practice, insofar as the nursing profession is concerned, of participative management was described in a 1980 Department of Health Report as follows: "The Working Party was concerned at the amount of representation and criticism it received regarding communication difficulties that exist at Health Board level between programme managers and matrons of hospitals, particularly in the general hospital care programmes. In voluntary hospitals, matrons do not feel isolated from their managing authority. Presumably the problem arises in Health Boards because of the remoteness of many hospitals from the management team which is based at Health Board headquarters: in many cases a distance of forty to fifty miles away from the hospital. Again in the case of voluntary hospitals, matron and top management are in a one-to-one situation whereas in the case of the Health Boards, the programme manager may have as many as twenty hospital units to look after, scattered over a radius of fifty miles or more from the Health Board headquarters. The same would apply as regards the other members of the management team, such as personnel officers, who might be expected to have frequent contact with matrons. The pattern of central management under the Health Board system causes difficulties in meeting the needs and problems of the nursing services especially as regards lack of involvement in staff appointments, in recruitment and in nurse education and training"[33]

The Irish Medical Organisation, in a report dated September 1987, considered that medical input into hospital decision-making was insufficient in public hospitals and that "this existing reality of reduced health care funding is the reason that more medical input to hospital administrative decisions is necessary. At a time of financial cutbacks the most appropriate groups to set priorities on spending are the professionals who are directly involved in delivering the medical services. Many traditional considerations must be seen in a flexible light in these changing times. The Medical Committee will therefore form the penultimate committee in the hospital with all personnel answerable to it directly or indirectly. The Medical Committee would participate in decisions relating to: 1) hospital planning and policy; 2) budget allocation and spending; 3) regular review of spending. The Medical Committee does not own any of the hospitals and therefore must be answerable to an Owner's Committee. The Owner's Committee would set the social and ethical priorities for the hospital. The exact services to be delivered over the period of any one year would take account of the needs of the community served by the hospital. The Medical Committee would set the medical priorities within the above Owner's Committee guidelines. It is important that this Medical Committee would have a relatively free hand to implement them. It is important that the Medical Committee would enact on a day-to-day, week-to-week and month-to-month basis how the hospital would be run. The Medical Committee would be seen as a body which is able to adjust the level of hospital services, including nursing, para-medical and auxiliary. Furthermore, the Committee should set priority on certain medical tests and treatments being delivered. The Chairman of the Medical Committee, or his/her deputy, would meet daily or as often as was necessary with the hospital matron and administrator"[34].

The Report also advocated the use of incentives: "it is further imperative that incentives be built into this activity at all levels. If the hospital as a whole performs well to budget, the savings must be available to it to improve the services as it sees proper. Each division within the hospital must be able to see what it can gain for its service by good adherence to its budget. Exceeding the budget will clearly be punished by proportionate lack of availability of funds subsequently"[35].

Incentives need not be monetary but can appeal to the professional base of the physician or administrator. Thus, for example, the managers of two large Dublin voluntary hospitals instanced that the cutbacks were reducing the capacity of their (largely foreign-trained) physicians to practice the latest skills and experience in their specialisms. The proposition that there is 'slack' within the hospital segment can be adduced from the following scenario. A consultant is appointed to 'head-up' a new or expanding department and resources (staff, space and equipment) are allocated to him. The lack of accountability for resource utilisation, either in the form of departmental budget or in monitoring use for 'eligible/non-eligible' patients, can lead to 'slack capture'. Thus, the measurement system, deficient as it is in the Irish system, and with an unmonitored 'public-private' mix, can lead to inevitable personal conflict of professional capacity and private remunerative gain. As one consultant stated: "the medical profession is loath to exercise peer-group review of colleagues in their use of resources"[36].

One feature of the training of Irish medical consultants is that a large number of them study and work abroad prior to their taking up appointments in this country. It is probable, therefore, that they will seek to practice at the level of these countries which have a higher technological base and greater economic capacity. The 'importation' of highly-skilled medical personnel into the Irish hospital system (based on, in large measure, the County Hospital system) has occasioned concern that the consultant's training may be inappropriate to the medical and economic environment of these hospitals. This issue was addressed by the Postgraduate Medical and Dental Board in a conference in 1983 on "Monospecialist Training and Multi-Disciplinary Needs". One Chief Executive Officer of a Health Board described the issue thus: "many hospitals which were hitherto staffed by general surgeons, who carried responsibility for all surgical cases presenting, found that as vacancies arose and new appointments were made the new appointees had little or no experience of or training in dealing with fractures, etc. (apart from some experience at junior level) and were naturally reluctant to carry the same range of responsibility as their predecessors. A new need was therefore created, not primarily by the requirements of patients but by the system of training being followed"[37].

Another issue raised was that the training structure of consultants was inappropriate and that, perhaps, more thought should be given to increasing the number of consultants relative to non-consultant hospital doctors (NcHDs). A Department of Health official stated: "in the period 1972 to 1981, the consultant establishment increased by over forty percent and the number of NCHD posts increased by eighty percent. Existing consultants have not been agreeable to share their NCHD staffs with new appointees and there was no evidence to suggest that their attitude in relation to this would change"[38].

The management practice of consultants in regard to their own junior staff is largely unstructured. A private consultancy study of medical practice in Irish hospitals found that, with few exceptions, it is at the consultant's personal instigation that rosters of junior staff are fixed. The report stated: "it is clear that there is considerable variation in the way different consultants prefer to work and run their department"[39]. In effect, therefore, the role of administrative management is diminished due to the scope of discretion available to consultants. Departmental budgets are largely the personnel costs of the staff delivering the service, and the report concluded that:

> "The current position is that NCHD budgets are held
> by the Secretary/Manager in most hospitals. This
> position means that Secretary/Managers are
> accountable for expenditure but not responsible for it,
> while consultants are responsible for expenditure but
> not accountable for it. There is no formal

requirement for consultants to control expenditure and any co-operation with management on this matter is dependent on the good nature of consultants wishing to help the overall financial position.

The introduction of clinical budgetting would impose managerial commitment on those responsible for committing the largest amount of expenditure in hospitals. This, of course, might or might not lead to changes in the organisation of medical activity in order to live within budgets".[40]

ALERNATIVE MANAGEMENT SYSTEMS

The management model outlined in 'Health - The Wider Dimensions' does not recommend change in the present structure of Irish health-care delivery. It acknowledges the need for greater co-ordination between the Health Boards and the public voluntary hospitals. It proposes change from a programme structure to 'geographic care areas', and for a strengthened planning function at all levels in the health system. Yet the Department of Health looks to the existing budget allocation process to achieve its objectives. That is, central allocation of expenditure and regional distribution of resources within the existing relationship of the 'vote' structure at national level will be utilised to implement the desired change. Indeed, the general stance of the proposals is for greater centralisation at national level. Given the data presented in this study, it is unlikely that such a model will generate the desired change.

The data on the Swedish system of management control and performance measurement set out in Chapters Four and Five provide an alternative model that could provide some guidance to the Irish health-care planners. The main features of the Swedish system are: local taxation and local control of the health care system (national allocation is some six percent of the total budget); hospital consultants (previously on a fee-per-service system) on a fixed salary set at the highest public service salary; regional allocation of hospital budgets for the acute hospitals, and pilot schemes for clinical budgets within the large acute hospitals, together with assessment of medical technology and quality care programmes.

An alternative model for hospital budgetting which is, perhaps, more aligned to the proposed 'geographic area' concept in 'Health - The Wider Dimensions' is that provided by the experience of Health Maintenance Organisations (HMOs) in the United States. The HMO model includes the following general characteristics: the HMO assumes a contractual responsibility to provide or ensure the delivery of a stated range of health services, including at least physician and hospital-care; it serves an enrolled, defined population; it has voluntary enrolment of subscribers, and requires a fixed periodic payment to the organisation that is independent of the use of services; there may be small charges related to utilisation, but these are relatively insignificant; it assumes at least part of the financial risk and/or gain in the provision of services.

The lower overall costs for the HMO enrollee seems to be primarily attributed to the lower rates of hospital use and it could, therefore, be seen as a method to constrain acute hospital costs in Ireland. Yet, as Luft observed, "it is clearly demonstrated that HMO performance cannot be evaluated independently from the structure of the medical care financing and policy environment", a caution which reflects this research's observations on the appropriateness of the DRG model in the Irish budget allocation environment (see Chapter Five). Luft further observes that "the mechanics... may be difficult in some systems, especially those in which the financing systems for physicians, in particular primary care physicians, and in-patient care are separate"[41]. This is, of course the position in Ireland.

While 'Health - The Wider Dimensions' observes that "the access to public hospital facilities extended to consultants under the Common Contract is seen to be inequitable and must be reviewed", it clearly considers that management structures can be altered without the substitution of incentives to the physicians which is demonstrably the basis of the incentive structure in the 'classic' HMO model (retention of savings due to decrease in hospitalisation)[42]. Indeed, the general thrust of 'The Wider Dimensions' is more dirigiste than anything suggested by the *laissez-faire* environment that gave rise to the incentive structures in the first instance, i.e. the United States. Back of this model is, of course, the dilemma of the central planner operating without clear policy objectives.

As Klein observes in a similar policy context in the NHS: "even when the centre did know best - even if governments did have clear views about what was desirable, it did not perceive itself to be in a position to command. It could educate, it could inspire and it could stimulate. To have done more would have run counter to the values both of localism and of professionalism"[43]. Indeed, the Minister for Health's decision to abolish the Local Advisory Committees in 1988 may well indicate that the concept of localism is now a lesser value than that of cost-savings[44]. More fundamental, perhaps, is the growing perception at the centre that it does 'know best' how to organise and manage.

CONCLUSION

The Department of Health and the Health Boards operate within an environment that is hierarchical in structure and decentralised in service delivery. The medical area is an uncertain decision-making environment where outcomes are problematic and whose base is scientific-technological. The civil service structure is characterised by stability, adherence to fixed 'decision-rules' and its base is generalist-technocratic. The exercise of control in this complex environment requires a clear exposition of the 'rules of the game' allied with measurement systems and incentives that allow for consensual appraisal of performance across a range of agreed measures, e.g. medical outcome, resource-use, retention of savings from efficient management. The Irish acute hospital segment, which has a weak decentralised decision-making structure, experienced the lack of such consensual arrangements in 1987.

The Department of Health had recourse to statutory provisions (Section 31 and 33 of the Health Act 1970) to ensure compliance with expenditure limits. The medical profession, whose education, training and management practice ill-equipped it to co-operate with its own members, sought to deflect the responsibility for cutbacks to the Department of Health. The President of the Irish Medical Organisation stated that:

> "Unfortunately, in the midst of the cuts, specific and unreasonable demands were imposed on our members which necessitated action to protect their rights. The threat of fines on GPs, who put quality of care before visiting rates, the offer to NCHDs of work without pay, the directive to consultants to travel long distances to see three to four patients, and the announcement that community care doctors should be replaced by lay civil servants were among the singular actions aimed against doctors which were indicative of the lack of any overall policy or strategy for developing the health services. The only explanation for these manoeuvres was that an attempt was being made to break the IMO and divide the profession. A reasoned and logical response by the IMO to these happenings was rejected by administration without any explanation - an aggressive and dictatorial attitude that is the order of the day. The IMO were left in the unenviable and undesirable position of having to take industrial action to protect their members and their families. We had a responsibility to defend these unprofessional attacks on our members and this we did to the best of our ability. The removal of dispensing from the rural GMS doctors was an unwarranted attack on the rural medical card patients which was also strongly opposed by the IMO".[45]

The Department of Health found itself in the paradoxical situation of being more in control of public voluntary hospitals (which they could close via the budget mechanism) than of the Health Board hospitals (where Health Boards could refuse to close a hospital). The measurement system only allowed for pro-rata cuts across the eight Health Boards even though it was acknowledged that regional disparities in medical and service facilities existed. The Department issued no detailed guidelines to hospitals and Health Boards to allow them to make reductions in accord with a national or regional plan. This was in part because there was no such plan and in part because the underdeveloped measurement system was not capable of providing indicators of performance.

The centre's assertion of control lay much more in the negative area of financial constraint than in a positive sense of directing and stimulating an organisation to respond to clear policy directives. One health service administrator described it as "the Department of Health feel that they must do the unpalatable, and then return to the Department of Finance; only at that stage will they get a listening"[46]. The increasing centralisation of decision making, rendered easier by the lack of a regional or local tax base, the absence of consensus within the Health Boards and the clear divide between administrative management and the professionals were not the desiderata prescribed by McKinsey. In large part, this was the result of the absence of a clear strategy and exacerbated by a resource allocation system that was more dependent on the availability of resources than on performance measured against agreed objectives.

It is characteristic of most recent Irish thinking on the health service that it has concentrated on achieving administrative efficiency in the absence of recognition of the need for a clear strategy on health service provision. Technocratic solutions are advanced without regard to the European experience of the efficacy of debate, research and experiment prior to clearly-drafted legislative statements of policy. To start from the administrative or, indeed, financial base is to opt for tactical, short-term, solutions which avoid the strategic issues at the heart of health-care policy.

FOOTNOTES

1. See, for example, **Report of the Institute for Research in the Social Sciences,** University of York, 1982-1987.

2. David G. Green, **Which Doctor?** IEA Research Monograph No. 40, 1985.

3. Personal communication, 1 July 1987.

4. Personal communication, 22 July 1987.

5. Department of Health, Arbitration Board L974, October 1974, paragraph 11.1.

6. Ibid, p.28.

7. Department of Health, **Report of the Working Party on the General Medical Service,** 1984, p.15.

8. A.D. Tussing, **Irish Medical Care Resources: An Economic Analysis,** ESRI, Paper No. 126, 1985, p.10.

9. Ibid, p.286.

10. Op. cit., p.25.

11. Personal communication, 18 May 1987.

12. Comhairle na nOspideal, **Second Report,** Jan. 1976-Dec. 1978, pp.23-24.

13. Comhairle na nOspideal, **Fourth Report,** June 1982-May 1985, p.3.

14. Comhairle na nOspideal, various reports.

15. Ibid.

16. See **Report of Chairman of Working Party on Pricing of the Common Contract.**

17. Personal Communication, June 1987.

18. **Working Party on a Common Contract and a Common Selection Procedure for Consultants,** Interim Report, p.4.

19. Ibid, p.20.

20. Ibid, p.4.

21. Ibid, p.5.

22. Ibid, p.6.

23. **Contract for Appointment of Consultant,** paragraph 7.3.

24. **Report of Chairman of Working Party on Pricing of Common Contract,** p.3.

25. Ibid, pp. 16 and 17.

26. Ibid, p.19.

27. Joint Oireachtas Report on State-Sponsored Bodies (9th Report), **Voluntary Health Insurance Board,** 1980, p.15.

28. **Ibid, p.77.**

29. Note of meeting, 16 June 1987.

30. See reports of the Voluntary Health Insurance Board.

31. It is important to recall that McKinsey did not recommend the administrative system - theier brief was to report on the structure as set out in the 1970 Health Act.

32. Department of Health, **Towards Better Health Care: Management in the Health Boards,** Volume II, 1970, Appendix E, p.E-2.

33. Department of Health, **Working Party on General Nursing,** 1980, p.78.

34. The Irish Medical Organisation, **Statement on some aspects of the Health Service,** 1987, p.38.

35. Ibid, p.39.

36. Personal communication, 5 June 1987.

37. Postgraduate Medical and Dental Board, **Report of Symposium on Monospecialist Training, Multidisciplinary Needs,** 1983, p.4.

38. Ibid, pp. 26-27.

39. PA Consultants, **Review of Medical Activities in Hospitals,** Vol.1, 1987, paragraph 3.2.2.

40. Ibid, paragraph 3.4.2.

41. H. Luft, **Alternative Delivery Systems,** OECD, Working Party on Social Policy, 1987, pp. 9 and 16.

42. Ibid.

43. R. Klein, **The Politics of the NHS, 1983, p.51.**

44. The proposals for reform of the health services administrative structure suggested by the larger opposition parties also present a similar centralisation of decision-making and a disregard for local participation.

45. K. Egan, "The Health Cuts and the Irish Medical Organisation", p.345, **Irish Medical Journal,** Vol. 80, No. 12, 1987.

46. Personal Communication, 17 December 1987.

CHAPTER SEVEN

Analysis

This study is largely concerned with the behaviour of individuals in an organisation when control is weak and the objectives of the enterprise are unclear or ill-defined. The 'uncertain' decision environment of the health sector was discussed in Chapter Three. Chapter Four described the administrative structure and control system adopted in Ireland in 1970 and its weakness in terms of performance measurement. The information system was underdeveloped and it did not assist in the governance of the professionals; indeed, the form of contract of the medical consultants precluded this possibility. Political decision-making is an important feature of any public service yet the 'rules of the game' in Ireland were quite different from those of the Netherlands and Sweden. Ill-defined goals or mission were never clarified, the legislative base of the service was weak and the administrative centre was unable to gain the authority and competence of their Dutch and Swedish counterparts. In large measure, the health service became a producer-oriented service with weak central control. The reassertion of central control over the finance function in 1987 did not alter the basic orientation of the health service; indeed, the financial instrument bluntly administered further divided the centre and the regions. Political decisions on expenditure allocation became the focus for national debate on a 'crisis' in the health service but the debate did not extend to an appraisal of the functions of the service and its administration. In 1970 there was a rush to reorganise and in 1988 a 'rush to rationalise'.

This chapter reviews the evidence and data presented in earlier chapters, evaluates the research propositions and considers their restatement in the light of this evidence. The comparative study of European countries is designed not to show anomalies in specific Irish cases but rather to describe common European problems in health care policy and administration. The particular features of the Irish system are responses to what are, in effect, shared international problems. That is, Ireland is unique not in its individual decisions but in its overall pattern of decision-making under similar environmental conditions.

The model and the research propositions are used to test the contention that the Irish health-care system, and the hospital segment thereof, lacks a control system which relates public investment to specific policy objectives. More specifically, the research proposition asserted that the Irish health-care system had no objective statement of its mission; that the hospital system has no defined role and no rational system of resource allocation; that its control system had developed no objective or measurable norms, and that professionals had created and captured slack for their own benefit; that the resource allocation system was highly centralised and lacked responsiveness to local needs, and there was no impetus to clarify the mission.

ASSESSMENT OF RESEARCH PROPOSITIONS

The proposition that 'the Irish health-care system has developed as a government-financed activity, yet it has operated without an objective statement of its mission' was intended to give the subsequent propositions internal coherence and it was not expected to yield much substantive data. The research perspective is concerned with the internal operations of the health-care system and the mission statement was seen primarily as an appraisal of government policy as it applied to health-care investments. Since Ireland's health-care system did not embrace the explicit provisions of the Welfare State (universality of access, free of charge at the point of use) it was assumed that policy statements and the measurement system would be directed at the specific objectives of the 'mixed' public-private characteristics of health care provision. Thus, if the State acknowledged the principle of free access to services for a designated part of the population, then the control system would be designed to ensure efficiency and effectiveness in this area of expenditure. Even allowing for the 'externalities' in any system of public expenditure (where provision of a facility such as a hospital is to be used by public and fee-paying patients), it would be seen as an important feature of control that performance measurement would related specifically to the efficacy of the public expenditures for the eligible patients. In addition, the costs involved in the provision of services would be monitored to ensure that there were no significant transfer of resources from the 'public' to the 'private' sector; or, if it was the case, that these costs would be recouped. The control system, as reflected in the Department of Health's circular letters and the published statistics, does not monitor the implementation of services for the eligible population. Public representatives, via parliamentary questions, do ask for the details of the provision of medical cards in individual cases but the monitoring of the quantum or quality of service has never been a specific concern of administrative or parliamentary action. There have been queries raised, in particular in recent years, as to the possible development of 'two-tier' medical care but such concern has not given rise to specific initiatives in monitoring the access of 'eligible' patients.

The official reports on the Irish health-care system are concerned primarily with efficiency; that is, the relationship between expenditure and output. The Irish data do not deal with issues such as the effectiveness of hospital care, the quality of care, or the effect of a reduction in hospital care in the absence of increased resources in alternative settings such as community care. This contrasts strongly with the Swedish statistical base in its monitoring of the effects of socio-economic status on health-care outcomes. Indeed, the very absence of a universal access provision to health services in the Irish context increases the potential burden of monitoring.[1] It also contrasts with the Dutch experience in monitoring resource usage by different categories of insured persons. Table 7.1 sets out the Dutch data in respect of 1986, and it demonstrates a role for the

State in a context where health-care expenditure is largely a private sector function.

Chapter Four described the 'job creation' programme in the health service during the period 1977-1980. Quite apart from the significant expenditures involved (which were increased due to the 'special pay' awards to health service personnel) the effect was that the government treated health-care as an instrument of economic policy, i.e. the provision of jobs. The programme, coming as it did after the failure to implement rationalisation in the hospital sector along the lines envisaged by the Fitzgerald Report, had a debilitating effect both on the administrative centre in the Departments of Health and Finance and on the hospitals themselves. Health-care, and jobs in the health service, was now seen as a 'cost-free' option. With the 'cutbacks' in 1987 and 1988, the implementation of service curtailment was a crude process especially when the criteria for service provision had, hitherto, been the availability of resources. The imposition of cash limits, enforced by way of Section 31 and Section 33 of the Health Act (1970), may be viewed as a necessary adjunct of macro-economic policy. Health-care policy, however, lacked any coherent rationale and the 'mission' was now one of adherence to budgetary targets.

At the aggregate, health-care policy in Ireland can be seen as part of a modernisation of the public service sector in the 1970's. In part, it was also a programme of administrative centralisation mirrored in the further decline of the functions of local administration. Its 'mission' was unarticulated, its legislative control was weak and the experience of the 1987 and 1988 'cutbacks' demonstrated the absence of a clear policy on service provision. The proposition that the Irish health-care system has developed as a government-financed activity, yet it has operated without an objective statement of its 'mission' is valid in the context of this research.

The proposition that "because of the lack of an objective, statement of mission of the Irish health-care system, the general hospital segment, either public or voluntary, has no defined role, and no rational system of resource allocation" is well supported by official statements, the experience of hospital planning and the data presented in earlier chapters. 'Health - The Wider Dimensions' states that the precise role of each hospital needs to be defined, that the relationship between the voluntary hospitals and the Health Boards requires clear definition and Comhairle na nOspideal acknowledges that the acute hospital system is still not a rational one.[2] These statements are made some seventeen years after the re-organisation was given effect in 1970.

Experience of hospital planning, either in pursuit of the Fitzgerald model or the altered (but unpublished) Comhairle na nOspideal/Department of Health proposals has demonstrated the difficulty in achieving rationalisation of acute hospitals.[3] The political composition of the Health Boards has, in some measure, blunted the technocratic intent of the administrative centre. The disuse and disregard of the Regional Hospital Boards ensured that the original Fitzgerald objective of national budgetting for acute hospitals, in three regions, was not achieved. The 'staffing-up' of the County Hospital system was, however, a function of the Comhairle while their retention was a political decision. The interplay of medicine and politics introduced considerable 'slack' into the system. 'Slack' can also be seen in the policy commitments or 'side payments' made to hospital consultants.[4] Their contract of employment, the lack of measurement within the system, and the ineffectiveness of the 'tripartite' model of hospital management combined to give unrestrained control over resource decisions to the medical sector. The 'cutback' phase in 1987 and 1988 demonstrated that the administrative centre had more control over the voluntary sector (by way of the direct budget relationship) that it enjoyed in the Health Board sector. As a direct result of the budgetary mechanism, the Department of Health could close voluntary hospitals; legally, of course, the closure is a decision for the hospital Board as the Department does not have jurisdiction in the actual closure decision. Evidence also suggests that the Department achieved some closures earlier than even they had planned. The 'rush' of events in 1987 overwhelmed the hospital segment and advantage was taken to achieve long-sought rationalisation proposals, e.g. Dr. Steven's Hospital in Dublin.[5]

The concept of regional self-sufficiency in hospital consultant staffing has recently been promoted by the Minister for Health and his officials.[6] It is not clear how the proposals will operate but it would seem that, in part, they are a reaction to the concern expressed by some Health Boards (notably the Western Health Board) over the 'transfer' of part of their budgets to the major Dublin voluntary hospitals. Comharile na nOspideal itself agrees that the rigidity in the budget system inhibits the dispersal of consultant manpower to under-resourced regions or specialisms. In part, this may confirm the original Fitzgerald model of three hospital regions with Regional Boards having budgetary competence. The politics of the hospital system may be contrasted with the system in Sweden where regional allocation of hospital budgets, which transcend the basic health system of the County Council, is a non-contentious issue. The lack of a local finance base in Ireland exacerbates the problem.

The 'programme' structure for general hospitals, divided into eight Health Board regions, is inadequate to take account of the geographical and medical reality of high technology hospitals. Sweden has seven hospital regions, Ireland has eight such regions. In Dublin, the dominance of the larger voluntary hospitals is now being eroded by the emergence of the joint-board hospitals and reduced public expenditures. If there was a failure to educate people on the original Fitzgerald proposals, it would now appear that a more covert programme of rationing is in operation. The utilisation of the budget instrument to establish a new hospital system runs counter to the original claims of devolved democratic representation for the Health Boards. It is also being done without a proper information system. No policy advice was given by the centre to the regions during the cutback phase and the framework of the budget system is rigid. The proposition that the Irish hospital sector has no defined role and no rational system of resource allocation is valid in the context of the data presented in this research.

The lack of rational system of resource allocation resulted in the control system developing 'no objective or measurable norms'. The bed-norm of the Fitzgerald Report (4.1 per 1,000 population) has now been revised to one of 3.7 per 1,000 population. Similarly, Comhairle na nOspideal have revised their own minimum consultant staffing norms to allow for the development of sub-specialities. The recommended consultant staff for a general hospital with 250 beds is three surgeons, three medical specialists and four anaesthetists.[7] These are, of course, input norms and they do not relate to the expected performance, financial or medical, of the hospital. The experience of the job creation programme further weakened any attempt to pursue the realisation of the norms in the staffing area. Thus, for example, the Report of the Working Party on General Nursing (1980) did not attempt to define appropriate staffing levels in different hospital care environments.

The budget review or audit process, as discussed in Chapter Five, is a cost-accounting procedure and it does not extend to any consideration of process efficiency. The Department of Health, faced with increasing demand on the hospital system, has sought to orient the control of hospital cost in two directions; the DRG system for hospital budgetting and the pursuit of explicit Admission Policies for the larger acute hospitals. Such evidence as does exist in the latter area suggests that undue hospitalisation, on medical criteria, has occurred. To date, no formal written admission procedures have been developed in the large acute hospitals.[8]

There is a tenuous linkage between the performance of a hospital (expressed in terms of bed-occupancy) and the hospital budget. Chapter Five found that no respondent in the study interviews saw any correlation between hospital activity and hospital budgets. The incremental budget model does, of course, allow for year-on-year increases which reflects the expenditure of the hospital in the previous year. This does not take formal account, however, of case-mix or new consultant appointments as the costing figures for hospital consultant appointments in Chapter Six demonstrated. That is, if the individual parts of the hospital are not subject to departmental budgetting, then the overall resources of the hospital may be subject to pressures in particular service departments, e.g. radiology and pathology. A study of a Radiology Department in a large acute public hospital in 1986 showed that, in the absence of agreed norms for x-ray usage between consultant firms in the hospital, the problem of service delivery was controlled by the way of the queue mechanism.[9] Indeed, the propensity to shift the focus of change to technical solutions (DRG, computer-based accounting systems) ignores the very real personnel and management issues that lie at the heart of complex organisations such as hospitals.

A DRG system which has been developed in the context of an 'open' system of funding (no predetermined cash limits) runs counter to the closed system of allocation that operates in Ireland.[10] It is also supported by peer-review mechanisms that are common medical practice in United States hospitals. It is, thus, a part of an overall system of governance rather than a once-off technical accounting innovation. Its effect, in the absence of budgetary and organisational change, would be to increase the total unit-cost operations of a hospital as medical staff responded to the pressure of reduced bed-stay by increasing bed throughput. In the absence of quality review procedures, it is possible that pressure to reduce bed-stay could impinge on the quality of patient care. No work has been done in this area in Ireland, yet it is a growing part of the Dutch and Swedish system of hospital care.[11] Pursuit of financial efficiency is a legitimate task of management, yet it has to be tempered by equal concern for product quality, especially in the context of alternative supplies, i.e. private health-care. The increase in subscriptions to the Voluntary Health Insurance Scheme in recent years may indicate public dissatisfaction with the perceived deterioration in quality of service in public hospitals.

Management's search for technical solutions has characterised recent health-care policy initiatives. The computer technology programme has not been successful (indeed, the larger voluntary hospitals developed their own in-house applications) nor has it extended beyond patient-admission systems in most of the larger acute public hospitals. The PA Consultancy Report on NCHD's found that management of resources was largely the remit of the hospital consultants, albeit that they were not, in formal sense, part of the management structure in the hospitals.[12] The absence of effectiveness or output measurement is a worldwide problem in hospital care but it is compounded in Ireland by a lack of a comprehensive information system that is supportive of both administrative and medical management. Incentives to economise are not available and, indeed, were not encouraged throughout the 1970's. The proposition that the control system has developed 'no objective or measurable norms' is thus well supported by the data and by the response of the decision-makers to resource constraints in the recent past.

The proposition that 'resource allocation is highly centralised in Dublin and the system lacks responsiveness to local health needs in the remainder of Ireland' requires restatement in the light of the data presented in earlier chapters. At the highest level of the accounting system for health services (The Health 'Vote'), there is no 'trade-off'between the programme budgets (Community Protection, Community Health Services, Community Welfare, Psychiatric, Handicapped, General Hospitals). The stance of the Department of Finance is that each programme is a separate and distinct entity and, therefore, a reduction in any area of expenditure does not allow for a concomitant increase in another part of the 'Vote'. It is difficult, therefore, to envisage how a strengthening of the Community Services programme can be made in the current 'stand still' of the overall health expenditure allocation.

The Department of Health has a direct funding relationship with voluntary hospitals, and each voluntary hospital budget is reviewed and approved on an individual basis. To a significant degree acute hospital services in the Eastern Health Board Region is in the domain of the Department. Indeed, the Health Board hospital consultants interviewed for this research all expressed the opinion that this direct relationship had, in the past benefitted the voluntary hospitals in Dublin.[13] With the 'cutback' in expenditures, however, the Department is now able to exert considerable pressure on these hospitals. The Department introduced a new form of accounts for these hospitals in 1987 which were not extended to the public hospital sector. In recent years, in the new hospitals in Dublin the form of management has changed from independent voluntary status to one of 'joint-board' hospitals (Beaumont, St. James', the proposed Tallaght hospital) where the Department is directly represented on the Board of Management. The proposals for hospital management in 'Health - The Wider Dimensions' also presage further structural change in the relationship between the Department and the voluntary hospital sector. This may well take the form of the Eastern Health Baord being the direct funding authority for the voluntary hospitals in the Dublin region. If, at present, in the words of one Department offical "that we are overwhelmed by detail" in respect of voluntary hospital funding, how will a shift to a Health Board structure yield results other than a reduction in day-to-day business?[14]

At Health Board level, the Department has advocated that the existing programme management system should be altered to one of 'geographic management'. (That is, "there is a need to move... to a system which relates resource allocation to health needs in particular catchment populations").[15] While the intent is not clear, it would appear that hospital management would retain its existing structure - that of a Programme Manager with hospital administrators in individual hospitals or groups of hospitals.

Yet, while resource allocation is centralised, resource disbursement and decision-making at regional level is a decentralised process. Indeed, one Chief Executive Officer remarked that the process was "so decentralised it would make you weep".[16]   This statement was made in the context of the propensity of Health Board members to involve themselves in the minutae of allocation decisions to local services.   The broad spectrum of Health Board's membership encourages highly localised involvement in hospital allocation decisions as they represent important local interests.   Thus, for example, the Southern Health Board's decision, rejecting its management team's advice, to retain capacity at Mallow and Bantry General Hospitals, involved further cutbacks at the Regional Hospital in Cork.[17]   Resource allocation is highly centralised and resource disbursement is a regionalised, highly localised, process at Health Board level.   In the absence of performance measurement and output data, the process is mediated through local representatives and Health Board management.   The allocation of medical consultant appointments was, for a long period, separate from the financial allocation process, even though these appointments involved significant resource commitment.   The data of Comhairle na nOspideal itself confirms the geographical imbalance of consultant appointments and the proposal to have 'regional self-sufficiency' would indicate the Department of Health's acknowledgement of this disparity.   The proposition is, therefore, valid but it requires modification in the context both of the disbursement process and the level of decision making.

The proposition that 'professionals within hospitals have created slack and captured that slack for their own benefit' requires some modification in the context of the data presented in earlier chapters.   Its most significant modification is the fact that political decision-making provided the impetus for slack creation.   Political decisions in the provision of specialist hospital services created an environment where slack creation was inevitable.   The job-creation programme (which included sanction for medical appointments) is one clear example of this process.   Another is the decision on the consultant Common Contract where the Department of Health itself did not have any clear goal in their negotiations, and the Minister for Health had a decisive influence on the decision. Political decision-making runs counter to the models of the health economists which stress the positive influence of the State to 'countervail' the influence of the medical profession.[18]

The term 'professional' includes all specialist staff involved in service delivery. Thus, for example, nursing, para-medical and technical staff also enjoyed significant benefits in remuneration and conditions of employment over and above that necessary to sustain the services. The lack of measurement in the Common Contract, the weak management control system in public hospitals, the use of public facilities without payment for privately insured patients (now at thirty percent of the population), and the acknowledged staffing-up of smaller hospitals with concomitant resource implications by Comhairle na nOspideal (where medical consultants are in a majority) all combine to give medical personnel an environment where individual decision-making is unregulated, and unaccountable, to management. The private practice provision in the Common Contract, with no ceiling on earnings and no supervision of resource usage for non-eligible patients, is an incentive to 'slack' capture. The average VHI earnings of consultants in 1986 was £24,000. This does not, of course, take account of the cost of the use of facilities in hospitals for the treatment of privately-insured patients. The medical consultant is the key decision-maker on resource usage in the hospital and the unregulated nature of these decisions provides an environment in Ireland, which lacks an effective information system, for significant slack creation and capture.

The response of the Irish Medical Organisation to the policy proposals in 'Health - The Wider Dimensions' (Chapter Four) demonstrates the divide between the technocratic view of the Department and the reaction of professional interests under threat. The concept of 'slack', particularly in a worldwide remunerative enterprise such as the practice of medicine, may be more germane in the area of policy than in remuneration. Thus, as Klein argues in the case of the NHS (Chapter Four) and

Milton and Roemer in the case of the United States (Chapter Two) the task is to devise control and management systems that will engage the medical profession in a co-operative fashion rather than the 'thou shalt not' forms of regulation. The attitude of both sides to the concept of information is instructive: administrators tend to view information as a locus of control while the professionals view it as a means to gain feedback on the efficacy of their efforts. The 'stand-off' written into the Common Contract on the lack of measurement must, therefore, be removed. It is the case that 'slack' will be depleted in times of constrained expenditure when resource allocation is tightened through a 'cash-limits' policy. With a rigid system of allocation, such as prevails in Irish health-care, this process could then impinge on the quality of care and, hence, performance measurement and norms become more relevant in this environment.[19] Incentives for the medical profession are required and these are discussed in the next chapter. The proposition that 'the professionals have created and captured slack' for their own benefit is valid especially in the area of control of policy formulation. It is equally the case, however, that political action and administrative weakness assisted this process.

The proposition that 'there is no impetus to clarify the mission of the health-care system as a whole' derives from the previous three propositions. It is the outcome of the process of policy making and administration described in earlier chapters. Chapter Four discussed the various recommendations and proposals in 'Health - The Wider Dimensions', the NESC document 'A Strategy for Development' and the targets of the World Health Organisation in its 'Health for All' programme. The response of the Swedish and Dutch governments was reviewed and it was shown that their response took the form of research, information gathering and policy proposals which were debated and promulgated long before any legislative or administrative change was contemplated and ratified. In the Irish case, it would appear that financial constraint is the primary impetus for change in the health-care system. Legislatively, it has been shown that the Irish system is weak both in strategic control and in performance measurement. The financial constraint experienced since 1981 in the health-care system has not resulted in significant policy proposals; political opinion appears to be that the 'mixed' system of public-private medical provision and State support for private health-care insurance is to remain.[20]

It is clear that strategic choice at a national level of decision-making does not preclude the development of information systems and performance measurement to ascertain the operational effect of these policies; the Dutch experience is pertinent in this regard. The uniqueness of the Irish response is the underdevelopment of the control system that would clarify and monitor the effects of strategic policy. It may well be that the 'cost-free' nature of medical service provision in the 1970's encouraged a disregard for information gathering and assessment; it is equally the case that the current push for technical solutions will result in further division between the 'controllers' and the providers of health care. The absence of quality control programmes, the acknowledged disparity in regional provision of some medical and dental services, will not be resolved via the financial instrument alone. It will require debate and clarification of the aims and objectives of health-care investment and the present evidence suggests that there is 'no impetus' in this regard.

The lack of impetus may well relate to the observed phenomenon that the higher socio-economic class (worldwide) are net beneficiaries of the public provision of services such as health care. Le Grand and Goodin observed that in health-care provision, even in 'nationalised' systems such as the NHS in Great Britain, the middle-classes consume, pro-rata, greater resources than those lower in the socio-economic scale.[21] In Ireland, the observed rise in VHI enrolment, the 'transfer' of resources implicit in the Common Contract, and the lack of measurement of services to the eligible sector, may well suit the majority of health-care consumers. From a public-choice perspective, therefore, the lack of impetus to clarify health-care strategy would be explicable by the majority gaining in the ill-defined service structure that exists in Irish health care.

CONCLUSION

What can Ireland learn from the experience of other European countries examined in this study? The most important lesson is to regard the investment decision in health-care as one which requires a clear strategic focus, supported through consistent action on the part of the administrative 'centre' and accompanied by consistent use of the means of influence available to the State. The political decision to invest in the Irish health services, without a clear strategic objective, severely restricted the State's capacity to control its investment decision. A producer-oriented system resulted and the 'rules of the game' were established as securing the maximum advantage for each interest group. The lack of performance measurement and the emphasis on cost-accounting (itself an underdeveloped function) contributed to 'slack creation' and restricted the potential return on the investment decision. The research propositions and data provide a focus for change in the Irish system of public health care investment, where, by its nature, there are few clear means-ends relationships. Such change requires the legislative definition of health-care investment strategy and the development of administrative control which will connect in financial and professional terms, public investment and health-care programmes. The next chapter outlines the necessary stages in this important area of public policy which will place Ireland on a par with other successful European countries.

FOOTNOTES

1. This point is also made by A.D. Tussing, **Irish Health Care Resources: An Economic Appraisal,** p.273.

2. See Comhairle na nOspideal, various reports, especially **Fourth Report,** June 1982-May 1985, pp. 3-4.

3. These hospital rationalisation plans were drawn up in 1987, but were not formally the subject of Ministerial or Government review.

4. 'Side Payments' are described by Cyert and March as "far from being incidental distribution of a fixed transferable booty, (they) represent the central process of goal specification. That is, a significant number of these payments are in the form of policy commitments".

5. Personal communications, 17th and 18th December, 1987.

6. See "Whiter the Acute Hospital System", address by Mr. J. O'Dwyer, Assistant Secretary, Department of Health.

7. Information received from Comhairle na nOspideal, 17 December 1987.

8. For data on this, see Department of Finance Reports - **An Analysis of the Trend Towards Increase in Hospitalisation,** October 1980, **A Review of Hospital Admissions Policy,** December 1984, and R. Hamill, **Short-Stay Hospital Patients in the Republic of Ireland,** Medical-Research Board, 1985.

9. **Department of Management, UCC,** December 1986.

10. On the basis of a fixed 'cash-limits' hospital budget, a DRG cost reimbursement procedure (with no pre-determined case-load) would inevitably lead to a breach in the cash-limits allocation.

11. See for example, SPRI "Listen to the Patients", SPRI Tryck 141, 1985.

12. PA Consultants, **Review of Medical Activities in Hospitals,** Vol. 1, 1987.

13. The data on financial control in the voluntary hospitals, outlined in Chapter Six, would appear to contradict this assumption.

14. The Department of Health would, it is true, now have an "arms length" relationship with the voluntary hospitals; this would not, however, assist in the strategic management process, in the absence of a national plan.

15. Department of Health, **Health - The Wider Dimensions, 1986, p.80.**

16. Personal communication, 11 November 1987.

17. See **Cork Examiner,** 22 August 1987.

18. An exception to the argument in David Green, **Challenge to the NHS,** where he argues the need for the State to reduce the monopolistic position of the doctor by way of deregulation of their licence-to-practice prerogative.

19. Cyert and March state that 'slack' operates to stabilise the system "by providing a pool of emergency resources, it permits aspirations to be maintained during relatively bad times".

20. No government, for example, has adopted the recommendation of the Commission on Taxation that tax-relief on private health insurance be abolished.

21. R.E. Goodin and J. Le Grant (ed), **Not Only the Poor - the Middle Class and the Welfare State,** 1987.

CHAPTER EIGHT

Conclusion

This Chapter discusses the implications of the study's findings and recommends changes to the Irish system of control that will improve the investment decision, provide a counter-balance to the influence of producer interests in health-care delivery, establish a framework for control similar to the record of successful European countries. A central stance of the recommendations is that control in health-care yields similar challenges to politicians, civil servants and health-care professionals under different financing systems for service delivery, as the data in this study has demonstrated. Control, **per se,** is rectificatory and not restorative; that is, it is about the maintenance of norms, the following of patterns and rules once these have been laid down. In Ireland, control was not seen in this way, largely because the legislative framework did not contain any explicit strategy and decisions on resource allocation were not related to specific objectives, nor were the performance of health service professionals subject to any sustained scrutiny. As a consequence, the information data-base did not extend beyond that of functional cost-accounting and it was inadequate to test for measures of return on the investment in health-care provision. The Swedish and Dutch systems, in contrast, share common features in their concern for explicitness in legislation, their attendance to the sovereign importance of measurement and information systems and their willingness to adapt and modify their control system to refocus their investment decisions. Control, as the evidence in this study demonstrates, is a complex issue and it requires more than the application of technical innovation in cost-accounting methods, the installation of computer-based information systems, or the imposition of "cash-limits" budgetary restraint. It is clear that, in Ireland, the alternative policy proposals, discussed in Chapter

Four, do not see the need for legislative change which would provide a framework for the investment decision. It is equally the case, as this study has demonstrated, that legislation provides in other European countries the basic control framework for health-care investment decisions. Such a framework incorporates performance measurement at the heart of the investment process and, hence, provides for greater accountability on the part of health service professionals. It is evident that the Irish model of administrative-based control has proved inadequate, that it runs directly counter to the experience of more successful European economies and that it provides no basis for a strategic redirection of health-care investment to the primary care level of the delivery system. Without appropriate legislation there is no impetus available to encourage the development of accountability and the health service will continue to be subject to the sway of the producer interests. Such an environment places Ireland on a par with underdeveloped nations and runs counter to the experience of more successful small modern economies.

LEGISLATIVE CHANGE

The study has described the complexity of the health-care environment and the need for legislative objectives, resource allocation models and management structures to be consistent with each other if strategic objectives are to be achieved and an adequate return on the investment realised. The recommendations for change in the Irish system should, therefore, be seen as a set of related propositions rather than as a series of options within the galaxy of possible choices open to policy makers. The recommendations are structured within the current political and social context in Ireland - that is, they seek to go with the grain of current thinking on health-care policy and service provision.

In evaluating legislative change, it is assumed that Ireland will continue to have a 'mixed' system of public and private support for health-care provision, although such an assumption does not exclude government scrutiny of the performance of the private sector as the data from the Netherlands has demonstrated. In the review of strategic objectives which are implicit in current Irish policy on service provision (see Chapter Four), the following are immediately recognisable as constituting the primary strategic basis for the investment in health-care provision:

(i)   that the primary care level (including community-based services) should be the basis of investment, and resources should be redirected from institutional-based services, i.e. hospitals;

(ii)   that no person should be deprived of care owing to lack of resources;

(iii) that there should be geographical equality in the distribution of health care resources.

The objectives are, in practice, the adoption of the principles of the World Health Organisation's 'Health for All' programme, a commitment to equalization of health incomes (as opposed to equalization of access) and the policy on resource distribution contained in the Department of Health's document 'Health - The Wider Dimensions'. They constitute, therefore, the basis for a revised legislative statement on health-care strategy and a framework for the investment decision. They provide the impetus for the installation of an information data-base through which the performance of administrators and professionals can be assessed, and the basis for a revised allocation system. These principles (or strategy) can be incorporated into legislation in a number of different ways.

Sweden and the Netherlands provide contrasting examples for incorporating investment decisions in a legislative framework, and they relate to their different systems of financial support for service delivery. The Swedish legislation - HS90 - is termed a 'Frame Law'; that is, it sets out the broad principles governing health-care (equality in supply of resources, both geographically and by social class, equality in access and utilization) and the task is devolved to the County Councils to achieve these objectives. In contrast, the Netherlands (with its private health-care insurance base) seeks to control the outcome through a complex series of legislative directives. This has led to tension between centralised decision-making and the freedom of action desired by individual enrolees in private insurance schemes. In both cases, Sweden and the Netherlands, have responded to the World Health Organisation's "Health for All" programme with detailed financial organisational and legislative initiatives to redirect resources to the primary care level. A similar response is found in Finland where the Primary Health Care Act 1972 aimed to increase the supply of primary care and to strengthen the role of the preventitive health services. In Ireland, the Swedish example of a 'Frame Law' would be appropriate as a legislative framework given the central financial support for the health system, and the decentralised nature of the regional Health Board structure.

How would such a revised legislative framework assist in the control of the Irish health-care system? Its most immediate effect would be to provide a framework for the investment decision; that is, the legislative objectives would focus investment in three main areas -geographical equality in supply of health-care resources, a strengthening of the primary care level, and the monitoring of health outcomes for the eligible (Category I - 'medical card' holders) section of the population. The legislation would facilitate implementation of the key strategic objectives of health-care policy by providing an impetus for a refocussed investment decision, embed the information requirement at the heart of the investment process, and monitor the allocation decision process that has given rise to a perception of a 'two-tier' health-care delivery system. The legislation would ensure that the resource allocation system, operated by the Departments of Finance and Health, was consistent with the strategic objectives; that is, the existing rigidities and barriers to redirection of resources inherent in the 'Vote' structure (see Chapter Five) would be abolished and the investment decision would be consistent with the legislative statement of objectives. Similarly, the commitment to equalisation of health outcomes would impact on the measurement of performance of hospital consultants as the primary functions of the Common Contract is medical care for the eligible sector of the population. A refocussed investment strategy, which is given legislative expression, would also change the 'rules of the game' for the relationship, on the one hand between the administrative 'centre' in Dublin and the Health Boards, and on the other hand between administration and the public. It would, in effect, replace the 'rule of men' by the 'rule of law' and bring Ireland's public sector investment process in line with that of modern European economies. It would provide an impetus for accountability on the part of producer interests that is not reliant on 'goodwill' or professional ethics but on the contractual relationship between employees and the employer, public servants and the State.

ORGANISATIONAL AND BUDGETARY CHANGE

The study has confirmed that the general hospital sector has no defined role and no rational system of resource allocation; that the measurement system has developed no objective or measurable norms, and that decision making is highly centralised in Dublin.

A revised legislative statement of health-care policy needs, therefore, to be supported by changes in the 'rules of the game' between the centre and the health-care regions. The primary 'means of influence' that can be used are the budget allocation system, the alteration of organisational structures and the measurement of performance. The resource allocation system never developed norms or performance measurement indicators largely due to 'slack' within the system, the division of the budgetary allocation function for hospitals between the Department of Health and the Health Boards, and the absence of measurement in the contract of employment for hospital consultants. In addition, the administrative profession is, itself, underdeveloped and Ireland has adopted an unusual stance compared with other countries in this case and neglects the need for a knowledge-based professionalism in health-care administration.

Information and measurement lies at the centre of the investment decision, and the Irish system needs to be upgraded to the level of other European countries. This is a threefold process; first, the budget system has to be more 'formula based' on norms and standards; second, the division of budgetary functions for hospitals has to be abolished, and third, administrative personnel have to be trained in the knowledge-based discipline of health-care administration. The refocussed budget system can be achieved through a modification of a DRG based model which would be adequate for control purposes, and by separating the budgets for Health Board acute general hospitals into a 'block' grant system to encourage accountability. Similarly, the voluntary hospitals should receive their budgets through the Health Boards to facilitate a unified hospital structure. There are no legal, medical or managerial arguments for the continuation of a dual budget mechanism and it further increases the undue centralisation of decision-making in the Irish system. Initially, the incremental budget model will be the norm for hospitals as it is evident that prospective budgets (which are insurance-based systems) are not consistent with the financing system in Ireland, which is a tax-based system.

The existing underdeveloped information framework has serious implications for local and regional autonomy if decision-making were to be further centralised in Dublin. Both the decentralised nature of health service delivery and the geographical, social and economic variations in the country require local discretion in the decision-making process. The 'failure', if such it is, of the existing weak decentralised Irish model owes far more to the absence of standards and norms that discipline decentralisation than it does to any defects in the model's appropriatness in a health-service environment. And, indeed, to increase centralisation, through, for example, some form of State-sponsored body to replace the Regional Health

Board structure would be to further increase the centralised decision-making structure. If one was to centralise, in the absence of a sophisticated information system which will take at least a decade to construct (the evidence from the NHS in Britain supports this time scale), the unresponsive character of resource allocation would greatly increase.

Indeed, further centralisation is difficult to envisage in practice as it is unclear what further functions would be transferred to Dublin. The tendency towards centralisation may well reflect the perceived impotence of the centre - in particular the Department of Health - at its failure to 'control' the decisions of the Health Boards and hospital management. Compliance is best achieved when the 'rules of the game' or policy limits are understood by all personnel within the organisation. Legislation, the development and promulgation of standards and norms, and the installation of performance measurement are not functions which can be dispensed with through recourse to administrative re-organisations such as the removal of the Health Board structure. The evidence from other countries confirms that, whatever the political choices made, a control system with these attributes is required. And the evidence also supports the contention that increasing decentralisation of decision-making is the European norm in health-care administration.

The study has identified the clear divide that exists between the administrative and professional class within the acute hospital sector (though it is less evident in the voluntary hospital sector). The Common Contract for hospital consultants institutionalises the divide as no accountability is possible within its existing framework, and this clearly requires revision. The contract would, in any event, require revision because of the increase in private health-care insurance since its negotiation and to measure the achievement of equalisation in health outcomes. The rise in private health-care insurance in the last ten years may reflect the development of a "two-tier" system in hospital provision, or at least in access to hospital services. In the absence of publicly-available data, such a development is difficult to confirm, although the use of publicly-funded facilities by consultants is certainly an additional incentive for private practice. The legislative commitment to equalisation of health outcomes requires the development of quality assurance programmes, as a necessary control on the potential transfer of resources. It is also required to allay fears that the "two-tier"system does not result in inequality in health outcomes on the basis of VHI membership.

Within the acute hospital sector there is a view, articulated forcibly by the medical profession, that the administrative personnel in charge of the acute public hospitals do not have adequate training or professional standing; the Department of Health officials also share this view. Health service administration is not recognised as a knowledge-based discipline in Ireland and consequently vocational training facilities are very inadequate. There has also been a growing tendency to question the value of administrative effort, and to see administration **per se** as a financial burden on the health service expenditure. This may be contrasted with Sweden and the Netherlands where approximately six percent of expenditure is devoted to administration and management, while the Irish figure is some 3.4 percent. Other countries (including the NHS in Great Britain) place a higher value on, and have a greater regard for, the management task within the health services. Barrington attributes the lack of impetus in this area to the fact that "the bureaucracy is too well adapted to the prevailing climate of wary anti-intellectualism and general scepticism about the efficacy of administrative self-consciousness".[1] A WHO survey of education and training programmes in health economics found only three locations in Ireland where the discipline was available (the Netherlands has thirteen such locations, Sweden has ten, including a graduate school for public health studies - the Nordic School, Gotenborg).

A central part of the administrative system that requires change is the relationship between Comhairle na nOspideal and the Department of Health. This would require legislative change and should be attended to in new legislation. The Comhairle should only have advisory status in relation to the regulation of consultant appointments and the decision to fund and approve such appointments should reside with the Minister for Health. Indeed, the de facto position since 1982 reflects this division of functions but it requires legislative confirmation.[2] In addition, within the 'block grant' allocation system recommended for the acute hospitals there should be specific recognition of the regional disparity in consultant provision. In this manner, An Comhairle could then redress the regional imbalance in appointments within the functional area of the hospitals.

In summary, the following changes are required in the administrative and organisation structure:

* revision of the Common Contract to reflect changes in private health insurance growth and to facilitate measurement of health outcomes;

* recognition of the central role of the Department of Health in the funding of consultant appointments - Comharile na nOspideal to have advisory status only;

* resource allocation decisions to take formal account of the regional disparities in consultant appointments.

In the absence of clearly defined performance measurement, the administrative system will respond only to the discipline of the budget. The medical profession may legitimately claim that such a stance ignores the human-base of their activity. When 'slack' was available in the system both sides could ignore the divide between them. The medical profession, especially the consultants who have trained in England and the United States, are familiar with quality assurance programmes and professional review techniques such as Peer-Review. No such scrutiny of administrative management exists other than the functional test of adherence to a cash-limits policy. The Department of Health has not pursued the issue of the development of norms and standards for service delivery nor is this matter yet on the agenda for debate. Such a development would discipline the administrative decision-making process. Installation of an effective information data-base would support the development of service norms and standards and provide legitimacy for administrative decisions. In addition, the statement of investment strategy in legislation would require administration to respond with measurement systems that would monitor progress to this end. Hence, the investment strategy would be a primary control on administrative action and it would discipline the present ad hoc system of control.

The recommendations are consistent with the data and evidence presented in this study. They are also consistent with the argument that publicly-funded Irish health-care requires legislative change to clarify its strategic base and that control should be seen as an outcome of consensual management rather than the **diktat** of central administration. The comparative focus of the research provides confirmation of the proposition that control in health-care is more than the sum of the parts of the management and accounting functions. The very uncertainty of medical intervention, its relationship to social and economic determinants, requires a management structure grounded in a consensual framework that is given expression in legislation.

The proposed changes will place Ireland's investment decisions in public health-care on a par with that of other European countries. They will provide a clearer and more accountable relationship between producer interests and the State, and, as a consequence, increase the responsiveness of the system. Measurement and information systems, directed towards the monitoring of clearly-defined strategic objectives, will constitute a revised set of 'rules of the game', and replace the present 'cash limits' approach with a model-based system directed towards the achievement of specific targets. The new decision-making environment should provide the basis for better quality at the existing level of resources. It is appropriate that such change is based on a management model that takes account of the diversity of individual behaviour and the conflicting claims of individual self-interest and organisational stability.

FOOTNOTES

1. T.J. Barrington, **The Irish Administrative System,** 1980, p.221.

2. See, Comhairle na nOspideal, **Fourth Report,** June 1982-May 1985 for a full discussion.

TABLE 1.1

CURRENT EXPENDITURE ON IRISH HEALTH SERVICES
1971 - 1987

Year (a)	Amount £ million
1970/71	77.47
1971/72	97.75
1972/73	153.63
1973/74	166.78
1974	200.69
1975	213.90
1976	261.45
1977	323.29
1978	414.03
1979	486.03
1980	666.20
1981	766.29
1982	851.92
1983	965.22
1984	1021.18
1985	1084.16
1986	1154.00
1987	1170.00

(a)   Year ending 31 March through 1973/74; year ending 31 December thereafter. Figures shown for 1973/74 and for 1974 overlap for three months.

Source: Appropriation Accounts; for 1986 and 1987, Estimates for the Public Service.

TABLE 1.2

PUBLIC SECTOR BORROWING REQUIREMENT
1975 - 1986

Year to 31 December	£ million
1975	674.6
1976	592.7
1977	702.6
1978	980.9
1979	1229.5
1980	1558.4
1981	2205.5
1982	2465.9
1983	2277.3
1984	2400.2
1985	2443.9
1986	2395.9

Source: Central Bank: Annual Report, 1986.

TABLE 2.1

HOSPITAL BEDS PER THOUSAND POPULATION

Country	Year to which figures relate	Beds per 1000 population
Sweden	1964	7.8
Luxembourg	1964	7.3
Ireland	1965/66	7.2
France	1963	6.9
Denmark	1964	6.6
Norway	1964	6.6
Switzerland	1964	6.2
Finland	1964	6.0
Scotland	1964	5.7
Northern Ireland	1964	5.5
Netherlands	1961/62	5.3
Belgium	1962	5.2
United States	1964	4.9
England and Wales	1964	4.3

Source: Fitzgerald Report, 1968.

TABLE 2.2

Acute Bed Requirements

Nature of Beds	Beds per 1000	Corresponding Scottish Figures
Community Beds		
General Medicine	0.8	0.8
General Surgery	0.8	0.8
Obstetrics	0.8	0.69
Gynaecology	0.3	0.3
TOTAL	2.7	
Regional Specialists		
Orthopaedics	0.33	0.33
Ophthalmology	0.06	0.06
E.N.T.	0.08	0.08
Infectious Diseases	0.1	0.3
Urology	0.8	0.08
Paediatrics	0.3	0.1
TOTAL	0.95	

TABLE 2.3

HOSPITAL BEDS AND HOSPITAL ADMISSIONS PER 1000 POPULATION
FOR EACH MEMBER STATE OF THE EEC 1960/70/76

Country	Hospital beds per 1000 population			Hospital Admissions per 1000 population		
	1960	1970	1976	1960	1970	1976
Belgium	4.3[a]	4.7[c]	6.4	n.a.	n.a.	n.a.
Denmark	6.0	6.1	6.4	116	141	172
France	7.6	7.8	8.1	n.a.	n.a.	168
Ger. Fed. Rep.	n.a.	9.4	10.0	n.a.	143	163
Ireland	6.2	6.1	5.8	106	125	162
Italy	6.7	8.5	8.6	88	150	171
Luxembourg	6.2	6.6	7.1	98	116	119[e]
Netherlands	4.8	5.3	5.2	80	92	104
U. K.	10.8[b]	9.7	8.7	92	113	115[d]

Note: The data in this table relate to general hospitals only, psychiatric hospitals are excluded. United Kingdom figures include nursing homes.

a	1962;	b	Excludes Scotland;
c	1971;	d	1974;
e	1975;	n.a.	not available.

Source: Social Indicators for the European Community 1960-1978 Eurostat.

TABLE 4.1

NUMBER OF MEDICAL CARDS AND PERCENTAGE OF POPULATION IN EACH COUNTY COVERED BY MEDICAL CARDS, 1984 AND 1985

Health Board and County	No of cards current on 31 Dec.		No of persons (inc. dependants) covered on 31 Dec.		Percentage of population covered on 31 Dec. 1985
	1985	1984	1985	1984	
EASTERN					
Dublin	148,985	144,815	264,296	254,625	26.35
Wicklow	16,452	17,096	30,517	31,416	34.90
Kildare	24,148	23,093	42,329	40,049	40.65
Total	189,585	185,004	337,142	326,090	28.22
MIDLAND					
Longford	7,865	7,672	15,885	15,981	51.01
Westmeath	14,068	13,704	25,765	25,400	41.88
Offaly	13,559	13,220	25,881	27,374	44.38
Laois	11,007	10,899	20,887	20,335	40.82
Total	46,499	45,495	88,418	89,090	43.74
MID-WESTERN					
Clare	17,332	16,826	29,193	28,297	33.34
Limerick	28,430	27,744	52,567	51,302	32.52
Tipperary (NR)	11,768	11,592	20,898	20,411	35.43
Total	57,530	56,162	102,658	100,010	33.31
NORTH EASTERN					
Cavan	13,926	13,377	23,654	22,613	43.92
Louth	21,347	19,896	40,542	39,861	45.90
Meath	19,362	18,751	38,455	37,046	40.30
Monaghan	11,999	12,244	21,803	22,428	42.59
Total	66,634	64,268	124,454	121,948	43.07
NORTH WESTERN					
Donegal	38,201	38,931	74,354	75,898	59.43
Leitrim	8,569	9,251	14,291	15,522	51.76
Sligo	13,164	14,434	23,019	25,021	41.50
Total	59,934	62,616	111,664	116,441	53.63
SOUTH EASTERN					
Carlow	10,757	10,604	21,186	20,540	53.20
Kilkenny	16,852	19,872	30,133	34,103	42.56
Tipperary (SR)	18,912	17,277	36,511	33,330	47.87
Waterford	18,409	18,173	32,550	32,151	36.74
Wexford	24,736	26,402	47,613	50,697	48.05
Total	89,666	92,328	167,993	170,821	44.85
SOUTHERN					
Cork	82,687	79,319	141,471	135,303	35.15
Kerry	31,671	30,694	57,332	55,809	46.70
Total	1114,358	110,013	198,803	191,112	37.85
WESTERN					
Galway	43,407	44,889	79,581	83,769	46.26
Mayo	34,306	35,495	63,834	68,645	55.62
Roscommon	16,225	17,015	28,726	31,239	52.67
Total	93,938	97,399	172,141	183,653	50.43
Grand Total	718,144	713,285	1,303,273	1,299,165	36.69

* The population figures for each area are taken from the 1981 census of population. The total population figure 3,552,000 is the official figure for 1985

TABLE 4.2

OCCUPATIONAL STRUCTURE OF HEALTH BOARDS
1971/1981

	1971*	1974	1977	1978	1979	1980	1981
Medical & Dental	1555	1400	2040	2019	2318	2395	2437
Nursing & Allied	11710	16286	17000	18650	19725	20611	21144
Paramedical	576	730	1145	1283	1430	1455	1695
Catering/ Housekeeping	5714	3467	4882	5308	5563	5731	6095
Maintenance	1488	1548	1642	1763	1746	1685	1837
Administration	1687	2308	2874	3318	3692	3834	4119
Other	1673	1547	2098	2025	2297	2347	2313
Total	24403	27286	31681	34366	36771	38058	39640

Source: Ross, Employment in the Public Domain in Recent Decades, page 189.

TABLE 4.3

OCCUPATIONAL STRUCTURE OF VOLUNTARY
HOSPITALS 1971 - 1981

	1971*	1974	1977	1978	1979	1980	1981
Medical & Dental	476	1359	1698	1816	1881	1953	1999
Nursing	5498	7814	8146	8355	8625	8861	9289
Paramedical	660	1054	1225	1275	1314	1359	1457
Catering/ Housekeeping	2118	2615	2749	2924	2966	3075	3113
Maintenance	252	381	396	445	465	473	500
Administration	859	1286	1391	1503	1543	1609	1772
Other	809	228	227	238	241	259	260
Total	10672	14737	14972	16556	17120	17589	18390

Source: Ross, Employment in the Public Domain in Recent
Decades, page 191.

TABLE 4.4

NUMBERS EMPLOYED: DEPARTMENT OF HEALTH
CENSUS FIGURES

Year	Nos. Submitted by Dept. of Finance Total Nos.	WTE	Nos. According to Health Data Department of Total Nos.	WTE	
1976	47,670	45,287	47,670	45,287	
1977	51,088	48,534	51,088	48,534	
1978	53,691	51,006	55,877	53,080	*1
1979	57,955	55,057	57,955	55,057	
1980	60,047	57,045	60,047	57,045	
1981	62,490	59,366	66,683	63,349	*2
1982	64,068	61,080	64,068	61,080	
1983	63,504	60,194	63,504	60,194	
1984	62,781	59,695	63,601	60,489	*3
1985	62,409	59,289	63,748	60,412	*4
1986	-	-	63,149	59,922	*5

1. 55,877 is the census number of persons employed in 1978. The WTE of 53,080 is calculated on the basis of WTE = 95% of numbers employed.
2. A special survey was conducted by the Department of Health in respect of staff employed on 21 July, 1981 the date on which the embargo on staffing took effect. This survey showed that 66,683 persons were employed. Assuming the WTE to be 95%, we calculated WTE as 63,349.
3. The figures submitted to the Department in respect of the March, 1984 census contained some estimates. The census conducted in September, 1984 produced a more accurate picture - i.e. 63,601 persons employed.
4. The 1985 figures in the Department of Finance document cite figures which were early 1985 estimates and were supplied as such to the Department of the Public Service on a provisional basis. The Department census at 31 March, 1985 shows 63,748 employed, with a wholetime equivalence of 60,412.
5. 1986 figures are at 24 January, 1986 and contain some estimates where data have not been received.

Source: Department of Finance, 1987.

TABLE 4.5

SWEDISH COUNTY COUNCIL INCOME, 1980

County Council Tax	64%
Tax equalization Grants	5%
State Contributions	9%
Compensation from other Principals	3%
Care and Treatment fees and insurance compensation	11%
Investment contribution from the State	1%
New Loans	1%
Other Income	6%
	___
	100

Source: Landsting forbundet: 1981 The County Councils and
        their Functions

TABLE 5.1

1982 Per Capita Expenditure on Medical Care

	Measured at current exchange rates	In US$ of 1982 Measured at current GDP purchasing power parity rates
Germany	874	883
Australia	828	796
Austria	644	684
Belgium	534	636
Canada	989	1058
Denmark	746	736
Spain	302	417
United States	1388	1388
Finland	692	629
France	391	996
Greece	187	256
Ireland	436	532
Iceland	865	832
Italy	441	607
Japan	602	673
Luxembourg	601	719
Norway	930	822
New Zealand	440	481
Netherlands	836	851
Portugal	132	248
United Kingdom	508	539
Sweden	1168	1239
Switzerland	1158	990

Source: OECD, Measuring Health Care, 1985.

TABLE 5.2

THE SHARE OF HEALTH EXPENDITURE IN NATIONAL EXPENDITURE, 1960 - 1983

	Percentage of total expenditure on Health in GNP						
	1960	1965	1970	1975	1980	1982	1983
Germany	4.8	5.1	5.6	8.1	8.1	8.2	8.2
Australia	5.1	5.3	5.7	7.6	7.4	7.6	7.5
Austria	4.4	4.7	5.3	6.4	7.0	7.3	7.3
Belgium	3.4	3.9	4.1	5.5	6.3	6.2	6.5
Canada	5.5	6.1	7.2	7.4	7.3	8.2	-
Denmark	3.6	4.8	6.1	6.5	6.8	6.8	6.6
Spain	-	2.7	4.1	5.1	5.9	6.3	-
United States	5.3	6.1	7.6	8.6	9.5	10.6	10.8
Finland	4.2	4.9	5.6	5.8	6.3	6.6	6.6
France	4.3	5.3	6.1	7.6	8.5	9.3	9.3
Greece	2.9	3.1	3.9	4.0	4.2	4.4	4.7
Ireland	4.0	4.4	5.6	7.7	8.7	8.2	-
Iceland	5.9	6.1	8.7	-	7.7	7.6	-
Italy	3.9	4.6	5.5	6.7	6.8	7.2	7.4
Japan	3.0	4.5	4.6	5.7	6.4	6.6	6.7
Luxembourg	-	-	4.9	5.9	6.6	6.5	-
Norway	3.3	3.9	5.0	6.7	6.8	6.8	6.9
New Zealand	4.4	-	4.5	5.2	5.7	5.7	-
Netherlands	3.9	4.4	6.0	7.7	8.3	8.7	8.8
Portugal	-	-	-	6.4	6.1	5.7	-
United Kingdom	3.9	4.2	4.5	5.5	5.8	5.9	6.2
Sweden	4.7	5.6	7.2	8.0	9.5	9.7	9.6
Switzerland	3.3	3.8	5.2	7.1	7.2	7.8	-
Turkey	-	-	-	-	-	-	-
OECD Average	4.1	4.7	5.6	6.7	7.2	7.4	7.6

Source: Measuring Health Care, 1960 - 1983, OECD, Paris, 1985.

TABLE 5.3

PUBLIC AND TOTAL HEALTH EXPENDITURES, 1960 - 1984 (Percent)

Country	1960 PH/TH	1960 TH/GDP	1965 PH/TH	1965 TH/GDP	1970 PH/TH	1970 TH/GDP	1975 PH/TH	1975 TH/GDP	1980 PH/TH	1980 TH/GDP	1984 PH/TH	1984 TH/GDP
Ireland	76.0	4.0	76.2	4.4	77.8	5.6	82.5	7.7	93.5	8.5	86.9	8.0
Netherlands	33.3	3.9	68.7	4.4	84.3	6.0	76.5	7.7	78.6	8.2	78.3	8.6
Sweden	72.6	4.7	79.5	5.6	86.0	7.2	90.2	8.0	92.0	9.5	91.4	9.4
U. K.	85.2	3.9	85.8	4.1	87.0	4.5	90.3	5.6	90.4	5.6	88.9	5.9
U. S.	24.7	5.3	26.2	6.1	37.0	7.6	42.5	8.6	42.5	9.5	41.4	10.7
Mean*	61.0	4.2	67.6	4.8	72.1	5.8	76.2	7.0	79.0	7.2	78.7	7.5
High/Low*	3.6	2.0	3.4	2.0	2.5	1.9	2.3	2.8	2.3	2.3	2.2	2.3
Standard Deviation*	18.2	0.8	15.8	0.8	15.8	1.2	13.6	1.5	13.6	1.3	12.2	1.5
Mean - Big Seven	60.3	4.4	64.4	5.1	70.9	5.8	74.3	7.0	73.9	7.4	72.9	8.0

Source::Adapted from Measuring Health Care 1960 - 1983, OECD, Paris, 1985.

Notes: PH = Public Health Expenditure; TH = Total Health Expenditure; GDP = Gross Domestic Product.

*   Excludes Luxembourg, New Zealand, Portugal, Spain and Switzerland.

Figures for 1984 are preliminary estimates.

TABLE 5.4

HOSPITAL REIMBURSEMENT AND FINANCING IN SELECTED OECD COUNTRIES

Country	Ownership of hospitals	Basis of Reimbursement for: Operating Costs	Capital Costs	The role of health sector planning
United Kingdom	Central governments National Health Service	Annual prospective global budgets controlled by the National Health Service (i.e. the central government)	Separate capital budgets controlled by the central government through the National Health Service	Regional and district Health Authorities develop health plans. Because the National Health Service owns all but the few private hospitals, the Health Authorities and central government fully determine the capacity of the hospital system
Netherlands	Local communities or lay boards of trustees	Until 1983 by negotiated per diems and charges; since 1984, by annual global budgets	Until 1983, the per diems, included amortization of capital costs. Since 1983, hospitals are reimbursed for capital costs via separately controlled line items in the budget	Construction of facilities and acquisition of major medical equipment requires a government-issued licence, which is issued on the basis of regional and national health sector planning.

TABLE 5.4 Cond.

HOSPITAL REIMBURSEMENT AND FINANCING IN SELECTED OECD COUNTRIES

Basis of Reimbursement for:

Country	Ownership of hospitals	Operating Costs	Capital Costs	The role of health sector planning
Sweden	Owned and operated by local community councils	Annual budgets, controlled by the local community councils	Community-financed, by means of specific appropriations voted by the community councils level.	The capacity of the hospital is planned and controlled at the community. There is no formal national health plan
United States	Over 60 per cent of all hospital beds are privately owned; 85 per cent are non-profit. The remainder are owned by federal, state and local governments	Prior to 1984, the federal Medicare Programme for the aged and disabled re-imbursed hospitals on the basis of retrospectively-determined reasonable costs. Since 1984 reimbursement is on the basis of prospectively-established payments per case (Diagnosis Related Groups-DRGs). Individual state Medicare Programmes use a variety of systems. Private insurers use a variety of approaches, predominantly retrospective cost or charge based	Under Medicare capital is currently reimbursed on a retrospective reasonable cost basis; but in the future is likely to be blended into the DRG rate. For other payers, reimburse-ment for capital is generally included in the payment rate. The principal governmental subsidies for capital are through the tax exemption of financing instruments for health care institutions	Planning is undertaken at state and local levels with some federal financial support. In most states and localities hospitals must obtain a "certificate of need" for opening of new beds or major acquisitions of equipment

Source: OECD Financing and Delivering Health Care, 1987.

TABLE 5.5

HOSPITAL ADMISSION RATES, 1960, 1970, 1980s (Percent of Population)

				Annual % of Change		
Country	1960	1970	1980s	1960-70	1970-80	1960-80s
Ireland			16.4 (82)			
Netherlands	8.6 (63)	10.0	11.8 (83)	2.3	1.4	1.9
Sweden	13.4	16.6	19.2 (83)	2.4	1.2	1.9
U. K.	9.2	11.3	12.7 (81)	2.3	1.1	1.8
U. S.	13.9	15.5	17.0 (81)	1.2	0.9	1.1
OECD						
Mean	10.4	12.5	15.3	2.9	2.1	2.7
Range	11.3	12.8	14.3	7.1	6.2	5.9
Standard Deviation	3.3	3.9	4.1	1.8	1.6	1.5

Source: Measuring Health Care 1960-1983, OECD, Paris, 1985, Table D.1(A).

TABLE 5.6

COSTS OF SELECTED CONSULTANT APPOINTMENTS

Post	Additional or Replacement	Start-Up Costs at 1981 levels £	Annual Running Cost at 1982 levels £
Obstetrician/Gynaecologist, Clonmel	Addl.	235,000	170,000
Physician, Mallow	Addl.	19,000	91,000
Surgeon, Mallow	Addl.	-	116,000
Surgeons, Mullingar	Addl. (1)	34,000	111,000
Anaesthetist, St. Vincents	Addl.	-	-
Geriatrician, St. Vincents	Addl.	283,000	299,000
Endocrinologist, St. Vincents	Repl.	47,800	49,500
Med. Oncologist, St. Vincents	Addl.	* N/A	158,000
Nuclear Med. Consultant, St. Vincents	Addl.	359,000	248,000
Respiratory Physician, CRH	Addl.	40,000	11,000
Paediatrician, CRH	Repl.	-	-
Geriatrician, CRH	Addl.	-	23,800
Clinical Haematologist, CRH	Repl.	* N/A	60,000
Endocrinologist, CRH	Addl.	19,000	34,000
Radiotherapist, CRH	Addl.	* N/A	26,000
Anaesthetist, CRH	Repl.	-	-
Urologist, Mater	Repl.	72,000	87,200
Gastro Enterologist, Mater	Repl.	40,000	5,000
A & E Consultant, Mater	Addl.	-	-
Anaesthetist, Mater	Repl.	-	-

Notes: (1) Pulmonary Laboratory likely to be equipped in 1982 at cost of £30,000.
           (2) Consultants salary is excluded in all cases.
          *   In the case of these posts the set-up costs are not readily identifiable.

Source: Department of Finance, October 1982.

TABLE 5.7

SUPPLEMENTARY ESTIMATES IN THE HEALTH SERVICE, 1973 - 1980

Year	A. Original[1] £ million	B. Supplementary £ million	B as and % of A £ million	Total £ million
1973/74	92.55	7.89	8.5%	100.44
1974 (Apr-Dec)	96.74	4.63	4.7%	101.87
1975	117.02	37.13	31.7%	154.15
1976	249.98	11.48	4.5%	261.46
1977	298.40	24.97	8.3%	323.37
1978	357.07	36.10	10.1%	393.17
1979	440.54	72.48	16.45%	513.02
1980	541.86	126.35	23.3%	668.21

1. This is a net figure; i.e. Gross total less appropriations-in-aid.

Source: Dail Debates, November 1981, Columns 1781 to 1796.

TABLE 5.8

PROJECTED AVERAGE ANNUAL INCREASE IN DUTCH HEALTH CARE EXPENDITURES

1986 - 2000

	Health Care Expenditures in Dutch Guilders (Millions)	Morbidity Quality	Health Care System	Total
Specialist Services	1.8	0.5	0.0	0.5
Administration	2.5	.05	0.0	0.5
Drugs	3.7	0.8	0.0	0.8
Hospital Care	20.5	1.4	0.1	1.3
Collective Preventive Care	5.9	0.8	0.5	1.01
Primary Health Care		0.7	1.2	1.9
Total	35.2	1.1	0.1	1.2

Source: WHO, Economic Strategies in Support of Health for All, 1987.

TABLE 6.1

CONSULTANT MANPOWER BY REGION, 1987

Consultant Establisment	Mid-West	South East	East	Mid-lands	North East	South East	North West	West
	68	165	527	44	57	79	46	109
% Population	8.9	15.2	34.8	5.9	8.5	10.9	6.0	9.8
% of Consultant Establisment	6.2	15.1	48.1	4.0	5.2	7.2	4.2	10.0

Source: Comhairle na nOspideal: Consultant Manpower Statistics, 1987.

TABLE 6.2

VACANT CONSULTANT POSTS IN 1987

	Mid-West	South	East	Mid-lands	North East	South East	North West	West	National
% Posts Vacant	8.8	5.5	5.1	9.1	5.3	13.9	6.5	11.0	6.8
No. of Posts Vacant	6	9	27	4	3	11	3	12	75

Source: Comhairle na nOspideal, Consultant Manpower Statistics, 1987.

TABLE 6.3

GROWTH IN MEMBERSHIP OF VOLUNTARY HEALTH
INSURANCE SCHEME

Year	Members	% Change Members	No of Claims	Claims per Member
1970/71	436,144	12.8	39,455	.090
1971/72	478,382	9.7	46,216	.097
1972/73	506,162	5.8	53,953	.107
1973/74	511,679	1.1	55,506	.108
1974/75	524,525	2.5	56,903	.108
1975/76	557,295	6.2	62,974	.113
1976/77	594,751	6.7	71,214	.120
1977/78	645,165	8.5	76,876	.119
1978/79	697,346	8.1	84,282	.121
1979/80	843,309	20.9	107,746	.128
1980/81	935,804	11.0	147,004	.157
1981/82	995,284	6.4	164,965	.166
1982/83	1,013,745	1.9	180,357	.178
1983/84	1,028,194	1.4	189,736	.185
1984/85	1,033,261	0.5	193,461	.187
1985/86	1,032,709	(0.1)	205,111	.199

Source: Voluntary Health Insurance Board.

TABLE 6.4

CHARGES PER DAY IN PUBLIC HOSPITALS

Year	Health Board Reg. Hosps and Voluntary Teaching Hosps		County Hosps & Voluntary Non-Teaching Hosps		District Hosps	
	Private	Semi-Private	Private	Semi-Private	Private	Semi-Private
1980	12.00	9.00	9.00	7.20	4.80	3.60
1981	14.40	10.80	10.80	8.65	5.75	4.30
1982	36.00	27.00	27.00	22.00	14.00	11.00
1983*	55.00	40.00	40.00	33.00	21.00	16.00
1984	69.00	50.00	50.00	41.00	26.00	20.00
1985	83.00	60.00	63.00	47.00	31.00	24.00
1986	88.00	63.50	67.00	50.00	33.00	25.00
1987	93.00	67.50	71.00	53.00	35.00	26.50
1988	96.00	70.00	73.50	55.00	36.00	27.50

* From 1983, includes Joint Board Teaching Hospitals.

Source: Department of Health.

199

TABLE 7.1

HOSPITAL ADMISSIONS IN 1 YEAR BY SEX AND TYPE OF INSURANCE

	Men		Women		Total Fund		Health Ins Insurance[1]		Private Health	
	Stf		Se		Stf		Se		Stf	

% persons who were admitted[2]

1981	6.2	(0.3)	7.5	(0.4)	6.8	(0.3)	7.2	(0.3)	6.0	(0.4)
1982	7.5	(0.4)	7.8	(0.4)	7.7	0.3)	8.5	(0.3)	5.9	(0.4)
1983	7.4	(0.4)	7.7	(0.4)	7.6	(0.3)	7.8	(0.3)	7.0	(0.5)
1984	7.5	(0.4)	7.6	(0.4)	7.5	(0.3)	7.9	(0.3)	6.8	(0.4)
1981/84	7.1	(0.2)	7.6	(0.2)	7.4	(0.1)	7.8	(0.2)	6.5	(0.2)

number of admissions per 100 persons in population[2]

1981	7.1	(0.4)	9.0	(0.5)	8.0	(0.3)	8.6	(0.4)	6.9	(0.5)
1982	8.7	(0.5)	9.6	(0.5)	9.1	(0.4)	10.0	(0.4)	7.4	(0.6)
1983	8.5	(0.5)	8.8	(0.5)	8.7	(0.3)	8.9	(0.4)	8.0	(0.5)
1984	9.3	(0.5)	8.7	(0.5)	9.0	(0.3)	9.6	(0.4)	8.1	(0.6)
1981/84	8.4	(0.2)	9.0	(0.2)	8.7	(0.2)	9.3	(0.2)	7.6	(0.3)

Source: Adapted from Compendium Gezondheidsstatistick Nederland, 1986.

Notes: 1   Including health insurance for Civil Servants.

2   Numbers may be underestimated, due to (among other things) memory effects.

FIGURE 2.1

CURRENT PUBLIC EXPENDITURE ON HEALTH
(At constant 1986 market prices)

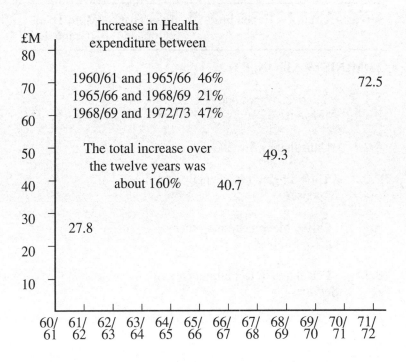

Source: Department of Health: Restructuring The Department
of Health, 1973.

FIGURE 5.1

SCHEMATIC VERSION OF APPROPRIATION ACCOUNTS
FOR THE HEALTH SERVICE (based on 1985 Accounts)

Service	Grant	Expenditure	Expenditure compared with Grant	
			Less Than Granted	More Than Granted

ADMINISTRATION, ETC.

A.1.   - Salaries, Wages and
        Allowances

A.2.   - Consultancy Services

B.1.   - Travelling and Incidental
        Expenses

B.2.   - Office Machinery and other
        Office Supplies

B.3.   - Postal and Telecommunications
        Services

C.   - Superintendent and District
        Registrars

D.   - Expenses in connection with
        the World Health Organisation
        and other International Bodies

E.   - Statutory Inquiries

F.   - Developmental, Consultative
        and Advisory Bodies

FIGURE 5.1 (continued)

Service	Grant	Expenditure	Expenditure compared with Grant	
			Less Than Granted	More Than Granted

GRANTS, ETC.

G.1. - Grants to Health Boards in respect of net expenditure (excluding expenditure on cash allowances and cash General Medical Services (Payments Board)
Original
Supplementary

G.2. - Grants to Health Boards in respect of expenditure on cash allowances and cash grants
Original
Supplementary

G.3. - Grants to Health Boards to meet expenses of the General Medical Services (Payments) Board
Original
Supplementary

G.4. - Grants on behalf of Health Boards to certain other Health Bodies
Original
Supplementary

FIGURE 5.1 (continued)

			Expenditure compared with Grant	
Service	Grant	Expenditure	Less Than Granted	More Than Granted

GRANTS, contd.

G.5. - Payments to Health Agencies in respect of balances of grants for years prior to 1985

G.6. - Payments in respect of disablement caused by Thalidomide

G.7. - Payments in respect of persons claiming to have been damaged by vaccination

G.8. - Grant to National Social Service Board

H. - Grants to Adoption Societies

I. - Grants to An Board Altranais

J. - The Irish Society for the Prevention of Cruelty to Children (Grant-in-Aid)

K. - Building, Equipping and Furnishing of Hospitals and other Health Facilities

FIGURE 5.1 (continued)

| Service | Grant | Expenditure | Expenditure compared with Grant | |
			Less Than Granted	More Than Granted

MISCELLANEOUS

L.   - Grant to Health Education Bureau

M.   - Dissemination of Information on Health and Health Services

N.   - Vaccine Lymph Supply

       Gross Total
       Original
       Supplementary

Deduct

0.   - Appropriations in Aid
       Original
       Less
       Supplementary

       Net Total
       Original
       Supplementary

FIGURE 5.2

Expenditure Allocation 1971-1987

Western Health Board

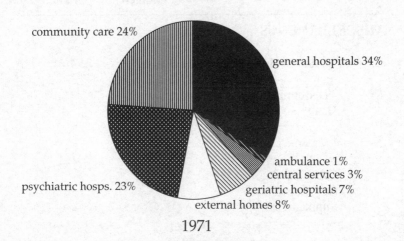

community care 24%

general hospitals 34%

ambulance 1%
central services 3%
geriatric hospitals 7%
external homes 8%

psychiatric hosps. 23%

1971

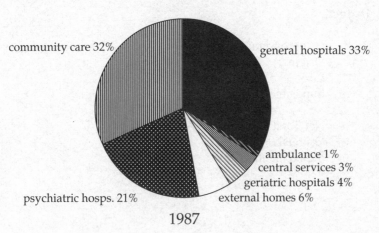

community care 32%

general hospitals 33%

ambulance 1%
central services 3%
geriatric hospitals 4%
external homes 6%

psychiatric hosps. 21%

1987

Source: Western Health board 1987

BIBLIOGRAPHY

Aaron, H.J. & Schwartz, W.B., **The Painful Prescription - Rationing Hospital Care,** Brookings Institution, Washington, 1984.

Abel-Smith, A., **Value for Money in the health services; a comparative study,** Heinemann, London, 1976.

Abel-Smith, A., **Cost-Containment in health care: a study of twelve European Countries,** Occasional Papers on Social Administration, No. 73, London, Bedford Sq. Press, 1984.

Alford, R., **Health Care Politics - Ideological and Interest Group Barriers to Reform,** University of Chicago Press, 1975.

Allen, David, **A Case Study of decision-making: the development of the 1962 hospital plan for England and Wales,** Manchester Business School, Working Paper Series No. 22.

Anthony, R. & Herzlinger R., **Management Control in Non-Profit Organizations,** Irwin, 1980.

Banta, H.D. & Kemp, K.B., **The Management of Health Care Technology in Nine Countries,** Spinger, New York, 1982.

Barr, A., Moores, B. & Rhys-Hearn, C., "A Review of the Various Methods of Measuring the dependency of patients on Nursing Staff", **International Journal of Nursing Studies,** Vol. 10, 1973, pp.195-208.

Barrington, R., **Health, Medicine and Politics in Ireland, 1900-1970** Institute of Public Administration, Dublin 1987.

Barington, T.J., **The Irish Administrative System,** Institute of Public Administration, Dublin 1980.

Bates, E.M., **Health Systems and Public Scrutiny,** Croom Helm, London 1983.

Boldy, D. (ed)., **Operations Research Applied to Health Services,** Croom Helm, London 1983.

Borgenhammar, E., **Health Care Budgetting; goals, structures, attitudes,** Stockholm School of Economics, 1979.

Bower, J.L., **Managing the Resource Allocation Process: A study of Corporate Planning and Investment,** Harvard Business School, Boston, 1970.

Blaney, R., "Applications of Evaluations in Acute Hospital Care", pp.93-107, in Holland, W. (ed) **Evaluation of Health Care,** Oxford University Press, 1983.

Bridgman, P.F., **Hospital Legislation,** Oxford University Press, 1979.

Bridgman, R.F. & Roemer, M.I., **Hospital Legislation and Hospital Systems,** World Health Organisation, Geneva, 1973.

Buchanan, J.M. & Wagner, R.E., (ed), **Fiscal Responsibility in Constitutional Democracy,** Leiden, Boston, 1978.

Buchanan, J.M. & Thirlby, G.F. (ed), **London School of Economics Essays on Cost,** L.S.E., London, 1973.

Buchanan, J.M., **Liberty Market and the State,** Wheatsheaf Books, London 1986.

Central Bureau of Statistics (Netherlands), **Vademecum of Health Statistics of the Netherlands,** 1984.

Central Bureau of Statistics (Netherlands), **Compendium of Health Statistics of the Netherlands,** 1986.

Child, J., **Organization: A Guide to Problems and Practice** (second edition), Harper and Row, London 1984.

Chubb, B., **The Government and Politics of Ireland,** Stanford University Press, 1970.

Cochrane, A.L., **Effectiveness and Efficiency: Random Reflections on Health Services,** Nuffield Provincial Hospitals Trust, 1972.

Cuddington, B., Palmquist, L., Trollinger, W., "Strategies for Survival in the Hospital Industry", pp.129-139, **Harvard Business Review,** May/June 1985.

Coombs, R.W., "Accounting for the Control of Doctors: Management Information Systems in Hospitals", **Accounting, Organizations and Society,** Vol. 12, No. 4, 1986, pp.389-404.

Collins, N., **Local Government Managers at Work,** Institute of Public Administration, Dublin, 1987.

Cooper, M.H., **Rationing Health Care,** Croom Helm, London, 1975.

Comharile na nOspideal, **First Report, September 1972 - December, 1975.**

Comharile na nOspideal, **Second Report, January 1976 - December 1978.**

Comharile na nOspideal, **Third Report, June 1979-May 1982**

Comharile na nOspideal, **Fourth Report, June 1982-May 1985**

Comharile na nOspideal, **Discussion Document on the Future Role of the Consultant,** 1982.

Comharile na nOspideal, **Consultant Manpower in the Republic of Ireland,** 1978-1984.

Comhairle na nOspideal, **Report on the Future Development of General Hospital Services - Cork City Area,** 1974.

Comharile na nOspideal, **Discussion Document on the Role of the Smaller Hospitals,** 1974.

Comharile na nOspideal, **Consultant Manpower Statistics as at 1st May, 1986.**

Comharile na nOspideal, **Consultant Manpower Statistics as at 1st May, 1987.**

Comharile na nOspideal, **Development of Diagnostic Radiological Services at Consultant Level,** 1980.

Commission of the European Communities, **Cost Containment in Health Care: The Experience of Twelve European Countries (1977-1983),** Luxembourg, 1984.

Crozier, M., **The Bureaucratic Phenomenon,** University of Chicago Press, 1984.

Curry, J., **The Irish Social Services,** Institute of Public Administration, Dublin 1980.

Cuyler, A., & Jonsson, S., (ed)., **Private and Public Health Services,** Basil Blackwell, Oxford, 1986.

Cuyler, A., **Need and the National Health Service,** Martin Robertson, London 1976.

Cyert, R.M., & March, J., **A Behavioural Theory of the Firm,** Prentice-Hall, N.J., 1963.

DHSS, **Common Waiting Lists for NHS and Private Patients in the NHS Hospitals,** HMSO, London (Cmnd. 6828) 1977.

Dutt, A.K., & Costa, F.J., **Public Planning in the Netherlands,** Oxford University Press, 1985.

Eckstein, H., **The English Health Service,** Harvard University Press, Boston 1964.

Egdahl, R.H., "Should we shrink the Health Care System", pp.125-134, **Harvard Business Review,** Jan/Feb., 1984.

Ellman, M., "The Crisis of the Welfare State - The Dutch Experience", pp.191-212, in Boulding, K. (ed), **The Economics of Human Betterment,** Macmillan Press, London 1984.

Fetter, R.B., Shin, Youngsoo, Freeman, J.L. et al, "Case Mix Definition by Diagnosis - Related Groups", Supplement to **Medical Care,** Vol. 18, No. 2, February 1980.

Finance, Department of, **Demand for Health Services by the over-65s,** (No. 50), 1977.

Finance, Department of, **Trends towards increase in Hospitalisation** (No. 73), 1980.

Finance, Department of, **Criteria for the Establishment of Health Centres** (No. 84), 1981.

Finance, Department of, **Resource Implications of Appointment of Hospital Consultants** (No. 105), 1982.

Finance, Department of, **Increase in Hospitalisation** (No. 107), 1982.

Finance, Department of, **Use of Five-Day Wards in General Hospitals** (No. 112), 1983.

Finance, Department of, **Review of Hospital Admissions Policy** (No. 121), 1984.

Finance, Department of, **Demand for Pathology Investigations,** (No. 119), 1984.

Fitzgerald, G.A., Beggan, M., and Drury, M.I., "Sources of Referral, Costs and length of Hospital Stay in a Teaching Hospital: Impact of a Day Care Facility", **Irish Medical Journal,** Vol. 74, No. 9, pp.265-270.

Foucault, M., **The Birth of the Clinic: An Archaeology of Medical Perception,** Tavistock Publications, London 1973.

Frist, T.J. Campbell, J.A., "Outlook for Hospitals: Systems are the Solution", **Harvard Business Review,** pp.130-141, Sept/Octob., 1981.

Goodin, R.E., & Le Grand, J. (ed), **Not only the Poor - The Middle Class and The Welfare State,** Allen and Unwin, London 1987.

Gray, A., & Jenkins, W.I., **Administrative Politics in British Government,** Wheatsheaf Books, London 1985.

Green, D.G., **Which Doctor?,** Institute of Economic Affairs, London 1985.

Green, D.G., **Challenge to the NHS,** Institute of Economic Affairs, London 1987.

Griffith, B., Iliffe, S., & Rayner C., **Banking on Sickness: Commercial Medicine in Britain and the USA,** Lawrence and Wishart, London 1987.

Health, Department of, **Working Party on General Nursing,** (Prl. 9156), 1980.

Health, Department of, **Report of the Working Party on the General Medicical Service,** (Pl. 2531), 1984.

Health, Department of, **The Psychiatric Services; Planning for The Future** (Pl. 3001), 1984.

Health, Department of, **Health Services,** 1983-1986.

Health, Department of, **Report of Inter-Departmental Committee on the Aged,** (Prl. 777), 1968.

Health, Department of, **Outline of the Future Hospital System, Report of the Consultative Council on the General Hospital Services** (Prl. 154), 1968.

Health, Department of, **The Health Services and their Further Development** (Prl. 8653), 1966.

Health, Department of, **Statistical Information Relevant to the Health Services,** for the years 1977, 1981, 1984 and 1985.

Health, Department of, **Health Statistics,** 1986.

Health, Department of, **Health: The Wider Dimensions; A Consultative Statement on Health Policy,** 1986.

Health, Department of, **A Review of the Irish Health Services,** 1975.

Hallas, J., "Acceptability in an Effectiveness and Efficiency Climate", pp. 81-105, in Long, A., and Harrison, S. (ed), **Health Services Efficiency,** Croom Helm, London 1985.

Harris, R., & Seldon, A., **Over-Ruled on Welfare,** Hobart Paperback, No. 13, 1979.

Hensey, B., **The Health Services of Ireland**, (Second Edition), Institute of Public Administration, Dublin 1972.

Herzlinger, R., & Schwartz, J., "How Companies tackle Health Care Costs", Part I, **Harvard Business Review,** pp.69-81, July/August 1985.

Holland, W. (ed), **Evaluation of Health Care,** Oxford University Press, Oxford 1983.

Hopwood, A., & Tomkins, C., **Issues in Public Sector Accounting, Phillip Allan, London 1984.**

Hospital Committee of the European Economic Community, **Methods of Cost Containment in Hospitals,** UC, Belgium, 1978.

Humphreys, P.C., **Public Service Employment: An Examination of Strategies in Ireland and other European Countries,** Institute of Public Adminsitration, Dublin 1983.

Illich, I, **Limits to Medicine,** Pelican Books, 1976.

Inbucon Management Consultants, **Community Care Review Report,** 1984.

Irish Medical Organisation, **Statement on Some Aspects of the Health Service,** 1987.

Irish Medical Journal, Vol. 80, No. 12, December 1987.

Ireland, **Building on Reality, 1985-1987,** (Pl. 2648), Dublin 1984.

Ireland, **Serving the Country Better, A White Paper on the Public Service** (Pl. 3262), Dublin 1985.

Ireland, **National Planning Board, Proposals for Plan 1984-1987** (Prl. 2309), Dublin 1984.

Ireland, **Review Body on Higher Remuneration in the Public Sector** (Report No. 20) (Prl. 8184), Dublin 1979.

Ireland, **The Devlin Report - A Summary,** Institute of Public Administration, Dublin 1970.

Ireland, **Report of the Review Body on the Organisation of Computerisation in the Government Services,** 1982.

Klastorin, T., Watts, C., "On the Measurement of Hospital Case Mix", pp. 675-685, **Medical Care,** Vol. 18, No. 6, 1980.

Klein, R., **The Politics of the National Health Service,** Longman, London 1983.

Lagergren, M., "Public Health Care Services in the Advanced Welfare State", pp.348-359, **Futures,** August, 1985.

Lambert, P.M., & Roger, F.H., (ed), **Hospital Statistics in Europe,** North Holland, 1982.

Le Grand, J., **The Strategy of Equality,** George Allen and Unwin, London 1982.

Le Grand, J., & Robinson, R., **Privatisation and the Welfare State,** George Allen and Unwin, London 1984.

Levin, A., (ed), **Regulating Health Care: The Struggle for Control,** Academy of Political Science, 1980.

Long, A., & Harrison, S., **Health Services Performance - Effectiveness and Efficiency,** Croom Helm, London 1985.

Luft, H., "How do Health-Maintenance Organisations Achieve their Savings", **New England Journal of Medicine,** Vol. 298, No. 4, June 1978, pp.1336-1343.

McCarthy, W.E.J., O'Brien, J.F., Dowd, V.G., **Wage Inflation and Wage Leadership,** ESRI, Paper No. 79, Dublin 1975.

McArthur, J.H. & Scott, B.R., **Industrial Planning in France,** Harvard Business School, Boston 1969.

Mason, W.B., Bedwell, C.L., Van Der Zwagg, R., & Runyan, J.W., "Why People are Hospitalised", **Medical Care,** Vol. 18, No. 2, 1980, pp.147-163.

Maxwell, R., **Health and Wealth: An Introduction to Health Care Spending,** Lexington Books, Mass. 1981.

March, J.G., & Simon, H.A., **Organizations,** John Wiley, New York 1958.

Maynard A., **Health Care in the European Community,** Croom Helm, London 1975.

Mendelsohn, R.S., **Confessions of a Medical Heretic,** Contemporary Books, Chicago 1979.

Midland Health Board, **Hospital Care Programme, Financial and Statistical Report,** 1986.

Midland Health Board, **Report of Review Body on Services for Mothers and Children,** 1986.

Midland Health Board, **Community Care Programme,** Report, 1986.

Ministry of Health, Welfare and Cultural Affairs, **Health as a Focal Point,** The Hague, 1987.

National Council for the Aged, **"It's Our Home", The Quality of Life in Private and Voluntary Nursing Homes,** Report No. 14, Dublin 1986.

National Council for the Aged, **Day Hospital Care,** Report No. 1, Dublin 1983.

National Council for the Aged, **Community Services for the Elderly,** Report No. 3, Dublin 1983.

National Health Council, **Reports for the Years Ended 31 March 1985 and 31 March 1986,** Dublin 1986.

National Economic and Social Council, **Some Major Issues in Health Policy,** Report No. 29, 1977.

National Economic and Social Council, **Universality and Selectivity: Strategies in Social Policy,** Report No. 36, 1978.

National Economic and Social Council, **Universality and Selectivity: Social Services in Ireland,** Report No. 38, 1978.

National Economic and Social Council, **Health Srvices: The Implications of Demographic Change,** Report No. 73, 1984.

National Economic and Social Council, **A Strategy for Development 1986-1990,** Report No. 83, 1986.

North-Western Health Board, **Allocation for Non-Capital Expenditure, 1988.**

North-Western Health Board, **Community Nursing Units, Proposals,** 1987.

North-Western Health Board, **Plan for Development of Psychiatric Services for Co. Donegal,** 1986.

O'Brien, J.F. **A Study of National Wage Agreements in Ireland,** ESRI, Paper No. 104, Dublin 1981.

Office of Health Economics, **Evaluation in the Health Services** (ed. W.A. Laing), 1972, OHE, London.

Office of Health Economics, **Health Expenditures in the U.K.,** 1986, OHE, London.

Office of Health Economics, **Scarce Resources in Health Care,** 1979, OHE, London.

Organisation for Economic Co-operation and Development, **The Welfare State in Crisis, Paris, 1981.**

Organisation for Economic Co-operation and Development, **Social Expenditure 1960-1990, Problems of Growth and Supply,** Paris 1985.

Organisation for Economic Co-operation and Development, **Measuring Health Care 1960-1983,** Paris 1985.

Organisation for Economic Co-operation and Development, **Living Conditions in OECD Countries,** Paris 1986.

Organisation for Economic Co-operation and Development, **Financing and Delivering Health Care,** Paris 1987.

Organisation for Economic Co-operation and Development, **Alternative Delivery Systems - Applicability of the United States Experience with Health Maintenance Organisations to other Countries,** MAS/WPI (87)05, by Professor H. Luft (unpublished).

PA Consultants, **Review of Medical Activities in Hospitals,** Vol. 1, 1987.

Page, E.C., & Goldsmith, M.J., **Central and Local Government Relations -A Comparative Analysis of West European Unitary States,** Sage Publications, London, 1987.

Postgraduate Medical and Dental Board, **Report on Symposium on Monospecialist Training - Multidisciplinary Needs, 1984.**

Postgraduate Medical and Dental Board, **Proceedings of Symposium on Postgraduate Medical and Dental Education in Ireland,** 1986.

Postgraduate Medical and Dental Board, **First Report,** March 1980-1985.

Rein, M., **From Policy to Practice,** Macmillian Press, London 1983.

Ro, Kong-Kyun, "Patient Characteristics, Hospital Characteristics and Hospital Use", pp.295-312, **Medical Care,** Vo.. VII, No. 4, July-August 1969.

Roemer, M.I., **Comparative National Policies on Health Care,** Marcel Drakken Inc., New York, 1977.

De Roo, A., **Client-Oriented Strategies in Dutch Health Care,** (unpublished), Erasmus University, 1986.

De Roo, A., "The Dutch Health System", in Saltman, R., (ed), **International Handbook of Health Care Systems,** Greenwood Press, Westport 1987.

Roche D., **Local Government in Ireland,** Institute of Public Administration, Dublin 1982.

Ross, M., **Employment in the Public Domain in Recent Decades,** ESRI, No. 127, 1986.

Rosen, M., **Epidemiology in Planning for Health,** University of Umea, SPRI 1987.

Russell, L.B., **Technology in Hospitals: Medical Advances and Their Diffusion,** Brookings Institution, Washington 1979.

Sherman, H., & Flatley, M., "Dissecting the Hospital Stay - A Method for Studying patient staging in Hospitals", **Medical Care,** Vol. 18, No. 7, 1980, pp.715-730.

Sweeney, T.K. & Ashley, J.S.A., "Forecasting Hospital Bed Needs", pp.331-334, **British Medical Journal,** Vol. 283, 1981.

Swedish Planning and Rationalisation Institute for Health & Social Services (SPRI), **Computerised Tomography in Sweden - Costs and Effects,** Stockholm, 1986.

Swedish Planning and Rationalisation Institute for Health & Social Services (SPRI), **How Can Medical Technology be Assessed?,** Stockholm 1985.

Swedish Planning and Rationalisation Institute for Health & Social Services (SPRI), **Must We Assess Medical Technology?,** Stockholm 1985.

Swedish Planning and Rationalisation Institute for Health & Social Services (SPRI), **Swedish Medical Care Programmes - for more efficient Medical Care,** Stockholm 1985.

Swedish Planning and Rationalisation Institute for Health & Social Services (SPRI), **Cost-Effectiveness Analyses in Health Care,** Stockholm 1985.

Swedish Planning and Rationalisation Institute for Health & Social Services (SPRI), **Planning for Health and Health Care - Findings from SPRI Projects in Gavleborg and Vasterbotten,** Stockholm 1986.

Swedish Planning and Rationalisation Institute for Health & Social Services (SPRI), **Economic Impact of Differences in Medical Practice,** Stockholm 1987.

Swedish Planning and Rationalisation Institute for Health & Social Services (SPRI), **Consensus Statement, Sight Improving Surgery,** Stockholm 1985.

SPRI, **Consensus Statement, Treatment of Myocarodial Infarction,** Stockholm 1985.

SPRI, **Consensus Statement, Treatment of Depressive Disorders,** Stockholm 1985.

SPRI, **Consensus Statement, Total Hip Joint Replacement,** Stockholm 1985.

SPRI, **Consensus Statement, Diagnostic Imaging of Liver** Stockholm 1985.

SPRI, **Consensus Statement, Urinary Incontinence in Adults,** Stockholm 1987.

Swedish Ministry of Health & Social Affairs, **The Swedish Health Services in the 1990s,** Stockholm 1982.

Swedish Board of Health and Welfare, **The Swedish Health Services in the 1980s,** Stockholm 1976.

Taylor, D. (ed), **Benefits and Risks in Medical Care,** Office of Health Economics, London 1974.

Thompson, J.D., **Organizations in Action,** McGraw-Hill, New York 1967.

Tierney, M., **The Parish Pump,** Able Press, Dublin 1982.

Tussing, A.D., **Irish Medical Care Resources: An Economic Analysis,** ESRI, Paper No. 126, 1985.

Van Atteueld, L., Broeders, C., and Lapre, R., "International Comparative Research in Health Care. A study of the literature", **Health Policy,** 8(1987), pp.105-136.

Western Health Board, **Plan for Development of Health Services, 1978-1982.**

Western Health Board, **Regional Hospital, Galway, Annual Report 1986.**

Western Health Board, **Annual Budget Report 1987.**

Western Health Board, **Allocation for Non-Capital Health Expenditure, 1988.**

World Health Organisation, **Research on Simulation Models for Health Management,** EURO Reports and Studies No. 20, Copenhagen 1979.

World Health Organisation, **Economic Research into Health Service Growth,** EURO Reports and Studies, No. 52, Copenhagen 1981.

World Health Organisation, **Guidelines for Health Care Practice in Relation to Cost-Effectiveness,** EURO Reports and Studies, No. 53, Copenhagen 1981.

World Health Organisation, **Control of Health Care Costs in Social Security Systems,** EURO Reports and Studies, No. 55, Copenhagen 1982.

World Health Organisation, **Economic Aspects of Communicable Diseases,** EURO Reports and Studies, No. 68, Copenhagen, 1982.

World Health Organisation, **Planning and Management for Health,** EURO Reports and Studies, No. 102, 1984.

World Health Organisation, **Developpment De La Formation En Economic Sanitaire,** Copenhagen 1986.

World Health Organisation, **Hospitals and Health for All,** Technical Report Series, Geneva 1987.

World Health Organisation, **Research for Health for All,** Vols. I and II, ICP/GPD 110/7, Copenhagen, April 1987.

World Health Organisation, **Continuity of Care for the Elderly,** ICP/HEE 217, Copenhagen, 1987.

World Health Organisation, **Targets for Health for All,** Copenhagen 1985.

World Health Organisation, **Economic Support for National Health for All Strategies,** A40/Technical Discussions, Geneva 1987.

World Health Organisation, **Health Policy Implications of Unemployment,** Copenhagen 1985.

World Health Organisation, **Migration and Health,** Copenhagen 1986.

World Health Organisation, **Financing Health Development - Options, Experience and Experiments,** WHO/HSC/87.1, Copenhagen 1987.

World Health Organisation, **Economic Support for National Health for All Strategies: Selected Bibliography,** WHO/HSC/87.2, Copenhagen 1987.

World Health Organisation, **The Management and Planning of Health Services,** Copenhagen 1982.

World Health Organisation, **Survey on Education and Training Programmes in Health Economics,** ICP/MPN, 503/s01, Copenhagen 1986.

Wrigley, L., **Ireland's Economic Problems,** (unpublished), 1986.

Wrigley, L., "Ireland in Economic Space", pp.66-83, in Lee, J.J. (ed), **Ireland: Towards a Sense of Place,** Cork University Press, 1985.

Van der Werff, A., **Health Services: Planning and Management for Health in the Netherlands,** Ministry of Welfare, Health and Culture, The Hague, 1984.

Yates, J., **Hospital Beds - A Problem for Diagnosis and Management,** Heinemann, London 1982.

Young, D., & Saltman, R., "Preventive Medicine for Hospital Costs", pp.126-133, **Harvard Business Review,** Jan/Feb., 1983.

INDEX

A

accounting systems, 14, 104-5, 161
    computer-based packages, 80, 99-100, 154, 155, 165
    lack of control system, 105-7
acute hospitals, 18, 23-4, 77, 100, 151
    and Dept of Health, 156
    management in, 132-7
    need for consensual appraisal, 139-40
    personnel divisions, 171-2
administration, 12-13, 85-6
    in acute hospitals, 132-7
    attitude to information, 113, 159
    and budgetting, 99
    characteristics of, 12, 18, 64-5, 79, 147, 161, 166, 169-70
    dissatisfaction, 132
    and eligibility, 87
    increased costs, 69-71
    and influence, 85-6, 92
    lack of professional standing, 172-3
    policy, 27-9, 76
    and quality of care, 75
    recommendations for change, 169-74
    resource allocation, 102-4
    staff-line relationships, 28, 57, 80, 103
Anthony, R and Herzlinger, R, 50
Arrow, Kenneth, 49
aural services, 85

B

Bantry General Hospital, 157
bargaining, 118, 809
Barrington, R, 12, 19, 59
Barrington, T J, 172
Battistella, R and Eastaugh, S, 48
Beaumont Hospital, 156

bed allocations, 23-4, 50, 84, 85, 99, 113
    in Fitzgerald Report, 153
    reduction of, 22 and VHI, 131
Blaney, R, 100
Borgenhammar, Prof E, 103
Bower, J L, 52
Bridgeman, R F and Roemer, M I, 62
British Medical Association (BMA), 121-2
budgetting, 66, 169
    alternative proposals, 137-9
    centralisation, 86
    and consultants, 124-7, 136-7
    deficiencies, 119, 152, 153, 170
    Health Boards, 69-71
    in hospitals, 44-5, 51-2, 134-5
    and measurement system, 92-3
    programme budgets, 104-7
    recommendations for change, 169-74
    resource allocation, 65, 97-100
Business Policy model, 9-10, 42

C

'capture' model, 118
centralisation, 43, 119, 120-1, 139, 147
    budgetting, 86
    of decision-making, 18, 33, 169
    effects of, 155-6, 170-1
    increasing, 12, 79, 80, 141
Chief Executive Officers, 70
    and budgetting, 105-6
    functions of, 72, 133
    quoted, 62, 63, 80, 104, 135-6, 156-7
    and Regional Hospital Boards, 23, 64
Child, J, 47
choice-of-doctor scheme, 25, 58
Comhairle na nOspideal, 18, 85, 113
    budgetary rigidity, 152
    and Dept of Health, 172-3

established, 26, 57
functions of, 20-21, 31, 68-9
and hospital structures, 64, 151
· and regional self-sufficiency, 157
restraints on, 123-5
Common Contract, 127-9, 157-8, 169
effects of, 171
lack of measurement in, 159
and private practice, 131, 138
transfer of resources, 160
community care, 1, 7, 56, 78, 81-2, 96-7, 140, 167
community health centres, 22
Comprehensive Public Expenditure Programmes, 104
Comptroller and Auditor General, 105
computer technology, 80, 99-100, 154, 155, 165
Confederation of Swedish County Councils, 110
consultants, 23, 29, 31, 68-9, 85, 123-4, 147, 153
and budgetting, 103
cost of appointments, 100-101, 127-9, 154
and cutbacks, 14
and Dept of Health, 173
geographical spread, 152, 157
and junior doctors, 8
management by, 68-9, 136
measurement of activity, 126-7, 129, 169
private practice, 126, 131, 138-9
quoted, 156
recommendations of, 19-20
remuneration, 125-7, 131
takeup of slack by, 44, 135, 151, 157-8
training of, 135-6
use of public facilities, 84, 172
and VHI, 130-1
Consultative Council on General Hospital Services, Report of.
see Fitzgerald Report
control system, 25-6, 46, 58
and 1970 Health Act, 56-7
deficiencies, 119, 160
effects of lack of, 141, 171
lack of, 11-12, 20, 105-7, 132, 148, 153, 155

district hospitals, 22, 85
Dr Steevens' Hospital, Dublin, 152
doctors, 8-9, 33, 78
    choice-of-doctor scheme, 58
    and cutbacks, 14-15, 140
    and GMS, 84, 121-3
    NCHDs, 136-7
    remuneration for GPs, 29
    role of, 8-9, 85
    training of, 5-6
Dutt, A K and Costa, F J, 67

E

Eastern Health Board, 121, 131, 156
Eckstein, H, 42-3
Economic Affairs, Institute for, 42
eligibility, 34, 135, 168
    and consultants, 126
    definition of, 59-60, 87
    not monitored, 85
employment, 70-71, 73(t), 74-5
Europe, 1
    comparisons with, 10-11, 27, 44, 95, 107, 147, 148
    lessons from, 161, 166

F

finance, 68. see also accounting; budgetting
    central control, 147
    cutbacks, 150
    decentralisation, 156-7
    Health vote, 104-5, 155, 168
    hospital budgetting, 153-4
    impetus for change, 160
    increased costs, 69-71, 105
    international comparisons, 95, 113-14
    measurement of expenditure, 92-114

eligibility in, 59-60
finance, 150
regionalisation, 62-3
Health Bill, 1969, 5
Health Boards, 26, 28, 57, 60, 65
accounting, 80
autonomy of, 77-8, 79
budget transfers, 152
budgetting, 31-2, 69-71, 100, 103, 104-5, 156, 169
and consultants, 124, 127-8
control system, 33
cutbacks, 76, 141
decentralisation, 168
deficiencies, 85
established, 62-3
functions of, 25, 29-30, 61-2, 69, 85
and GMS costs, 122-3
lack of control, 105
management system, 132, 156
numbers employed, 75
personnel grading structure, 71-2
relationships with Dept of Health, 103-4
relationships with hospitals, 63-4, 77, 108, 133, 137, 141, 151
resource allocation, 156-7
service delivery, 102
health care policy, 1-2, 7, 11-12, 58, 63, 64, 66-7. see
also mission statement in 1970 Health Act, 60-61
accountability, 32-4
administrative control, 27-9, 28
analysis, 9-11, 147-61
assessment of, 1, 42-53
bed allocation criteria, 23-4
centralising tendency, 42-3
and cutbacks, 152-3
deficiencies, 42, 76, 101-02
Department's review of, 76-9
history of, 19-27
impetus for change, 160
lack of, 6, 10, 18, 103-4, 107, 141-2
national strategies, 56-87

I

Inbucon/AIC Management Consultants, 127
influence, means of, 9-10, 44, 47, 51, 92, 169
information, 147
    attitudes to, 113, 159
    characteristic of control, 47-8
    effects of lack of, 41, 100, 155
    lack of, 13, 85, 92, 99
    limitations of, 165
    necessity for, 7, 160, 170
    recommendations, 167, 174
Institute of Economic Affairs (IEA), 118-19
insurance. see health insurance
investment decision process, 4
Irish Local Government Officials Union, 71
Irish Management Institute (IMI), 127
Irish Medical Organisation (IMO), 79-80, 86, 158
    on cutbacks, 140
    Report, 1987, 133-5
Irish Medical Union (IMU), 130

J

Japan, 95
job creation, 150, 157
    as alternative mission, 69-76
joint-board hospitals, 152, 156
judgemental strategy, 49-50
junior hospital doctors, 8

K

Klein, R, 20, 68, 113, 139, 159

L

Le Grand, J and Goodin, R E, 160
legislative framework, 44, 58-65, 76, 87. see also
    Health Acts
    aims of, 121
    and budgetting, 98
    deficiencies of, 62, 108, 147
    effects of lack of, 32-3, 57, 65
    importance of, 11-12, 86, 161, 166
    lack of, 13, 27-8
    lack of strategy, 102-3
    recommendations, 166-9, 174
life-style illnesses, 96
Local Advisory Committees, 26, 132, 139
Local Government and Public Services Union (LGPSU), 71
Luft, H, 101, 138

M

McAuto, 99
McKinsey and Company, 80, 141
    on performance indicators, 103-4
    recommendations, 28-9, 70, 104, 132, 133
Mallow General Hospital, 157
management system, 99
    alternative systems, 137-9
    characteristics of, 79
    function of, 92-3
    for health care, 118-42
    need for performance indicators, 103-4
    no criteria for, 101-02
    and personnel, 159
    problems of, 98
    staff-line, 80, 103
March, J G and Simon, H A, 8-9
Maynard, A, 26
measurement system, 75, 82
    characteristics of, 79

administration, 165, 172
bed allocation, 99
defined mission, 57
financing, 112
hospital budgetting, 154
legislation, 65, 110-11, 167-8
monitoring, 149-50
performance measurement, 46, 82, 160
and private medicine, 167
research, 159
non-consultant hospital doctors (NCHDs), 136-7, 140, 155
Nordic School, Gotenburg, 172
North-Eastern Health Board, 131
North-Western Health Board, 131
Northern Ireland, 24
Norway, 95

O

OECD study, 95, 97
O'Mahony, D, 58
opthalmic services, 85

P

PA Consultancy Report, 155
patients. see eligibility
pay, 75, 105, 107, 120, 122-7
Peer Review, 113, 154, 173
personnel, 13, 68-9, 73(t), 74-5, 110, 112, 133, 158, 159.
    see also consultants
    administrative, 12-13
    and budgetting, 52
    control of, 21
    cost of recruitment, 74
    divisions among, 14-15, 28, 132, 171-2
    and expenditure, 97-8
    grading structure, 71-2

increase in, 70-71, 124-5
influence of, 20
and management, 78
manpower policies, 84
need for greater accountability, 166
regional self-sufficiency, 152
remuneration, 75, 105, 107, 120, 122-7
role of, 85, 118
personnel officers, 133
planning, 120-1
Postgraduate Medical and Dental Board, 135-6
preventative medicine, 6, 56, 96
primary care, 1, 13, 77, 123
private medicine, 8, 110, 126, 154, 160
growth in, 12
relationship with public medicine, 160-1, 166-7
transfer of resources to, 148-9
use of public facilities, 12, 84, 158, 172
Programme Managers, 70, 133, 156
public sector borrowing requirement, 4-5
public sector recruitment embargo, 71-2
Public Service, White Paper on, 28
Public Services Organisation Review Group (PSORG), 27-8, 98
public voluntary hospitals, 125, 125-7, 132, 141

Q

quality of care, 159, 160, 172

R

radiology, 154
rationalisation, 18, 150, 151
Regional Hospital, Cork, 157
Regional Hospital Boards, 18, 57, 108, 121, 151
established, 26
functions, 63-5
regional hospitals, 104-5

regionalisation, 63, 87, 108, 120-1, 132, 160. see also
    Health Boards
research model
    comparative focus, 46-7
resource allocation, 51-2, 57, 78-9, 105, 151
    and administration, 102-4
    centralised, 119, 120-1
    debate on, 132
    decentralised, 156-7
    and Dept of Health, 65
    and Health Boards, 63-4
    hospital budgets, 77, 97-100
    lack of measurement system, 92-7, 141, 148, 153
    from public to private medicine, 160-1
    recommendations, 167, 168-9
    and regional hospitals, 108
rules of the game, 45, 114, 147, 161
    changed, 169, 174
    effects of, 171
    form of influence, 10
    need for agreement, 29, 50, 65, 93, 139

S

St James's Hospital, 156
Scotland, 24
Scott, B R and McArthur, J, 51
Scott, Bruce, 9-10, 43-4
service delivery, 60, 102, 132, 154
    decentralised, 139
    failure to define, 61-2, 76
    inequalities, 168
    lack of standards, 50
Sickness Funds Insurance Act (Netherlands), 66
slack, 63, 92, 118, 135
    concept of, 158-9
    creation of, 57, 151, 161
    effects of, 169, 173
    takeup of, 44, 119, 148, 157-8

South-Eastern Health Board, 131
Southern Health Board, 131, 157
Spain, 95
staff. see personnel
State
   and medical care strategies, 119
   need for consistent policy, 58
   in The Netherlands, 67-8
   in research model, 45
   role of, 11-13, 25-6, 32-3, 113, 119, 148-9
'Strategy for Development 1986-1990' (NESC), 5-6, 6-7, 83-6, 159
supplementary estimates, 58, 105
Supreme Court, 60-61
Sweden, 11, 12, 19, 46, 87, 95, 107, 137-8
   acute hospital services, 108-10
   administration, 165, 172
   bed allocation, 99
   budgetting, 98, 103, 152, 154
   defined mission, 57
   Gottenburg region, 108-10
   HS-90, 83, 110, 112, 167-8
   interviews, 45
   legislation, 65, 81-3, 102, 167-8
   measurement system, 81, 82, 102
   monitoring, 149
   research, 159
Swedish Planning and Rationalisation Institute for Health and
   Social Services (SPRI), 111-12

T

Tallaght hospital, 156
Thompson, J D, 49-50
trade-offs, 52
trade unions, 14-15, 68
Tussing, A Dale, 83, 84-5, 122